AUTOMATION AND SOCIETY

*A continuing forum of advanced thinking
concerning the role of automation in
society, future planning, and the critical
concept of the introduction of technological
change.*

First Annual Symposium on Automation and Society co-sponsored by
the University of Georgia and the Reliance Electric Company

THE GEORGIA-
RELIANCE SYMPOSIUM

AUTOMATION AND SOCIETY

edited by

ELLIS L. SCOTT and ROGER W. BOLZ

published by

The Center for the Study of Automation and Society

Athens, Georgia

Preface

The best criterion for judging the initial value of a conference is the reaction of those who were there. On this basis, the First Annual Symposium on Automation and Society was an immense success. The participants, each contributing a valuable three days, felt it was one of the most stimulating conferences they had attended. A typical response could serve to summarize the meeting; "a lot of new or enlarged thinking about the role of automation in society, future planning, and the whole concept of technological change."

The participants were also challenged by the symposium. I use the word knowing that all of us are invited to be challenged by important issues coming to our attention almost daily. But very definitely the reasoned discussion at the symposium did carry a challenge to each participant: how to better understand and apply the wealth of technology that is available and how to apply it in the interest of society as a whole; how to make the educational system more flexible in meeting a technological society's requirements; the challenge to plan in depth for the impact that increasing automation will have on business organization and the economic structure; the challenge to be imaginative in visualizing social changes that lie ahead and creating new social organizations and practices in harmony with these changes.

Big challenges, within even larger issues, are in sharper focus as a result of this first full examination made at the

symposium. This book is based on ideas developed at the symposium. Future symposia and related projects will help to extend, refine and apply the new thinking being done on the vital subject of automation.

Ellis L. Scott
Symposium Chairman

Contents

Automation
and
Society

1

A Look Ahead

Fred C. Davison

Fred C. Davison, President of the University of Georgia, received his DVM degree from the University of Georgia and his Ph.D. from Iowa State University. Following a period on the teaching staff at Iowa State University he was associated with the Institute for Atomic Research. He was appointed a member of the Scientific Staff of the American Veterinary Medicine Association in Chicago and subsequently served as Dean of the University of Georgia School of Veterinary Medicine and as Vice Chancellor of the University System of Georgia. In 1967 he became the seventeenth President of the University of Georgia — the nation's oldest chartered state university.

Automation and Society is a topic of wide current interest and great promise. The first symposium brought to the campus of the University of Georgia representatives from industry, education, government, and other areas of public life. The pervasiveness of interest in automation is reflected in the heterogeneity of the participants in the symposium. These included practitioners — men on the technological frontier coping with problems of automation on a day to day basis; scholars from many disciplines — men with responsibilities for formulating public policy in this vital area; and men from the communications field who affect public opinion. The symposium group, about 50 in number, represented many important segments of our society.

Clearing the Picture

These conferees are leading authorities in four broad fields: social organization, automation technology itself, education, and business and the economy. It was their mission to discuss the state of the art of the technology and its relationships with areas of social concern. The symposium provided a forum for clearing away misconceptions about automation. It offered an opportunity to develop a better picture of automation's potential and pitfalls, based on current facts and reasoned opinion from different points of view.

Four featured speakers participated in the symposium. Theodore A. Smith, Executive Vice President of RCA, was the keynoter. He set the stage for the three day series of discussions to follow. Mr. Smith's long and distinguished association with advanced technology made him a particularly appropriate keynote speaker. Featured speaker for the first public session was Vice Admiral Hyman G. Rickover. Admiral Rickover, who carries responsibilities with both the United States Navy and Atomic Energy Commission, compellingly argued for a humanistic technology to serve man's interest. Technology, Admiral Rickover maintained, "may even enable man to become more truly human than it has ever been possible for him to be." A change of pace was provided for the second public session by the late Dr. Willy Ley. Dr. Ley reminded us again of a fast changing technology and how the concept of the "foreseeable future" may have been shortened to a span of no more than five years. Summarizing the sense of the symposium and emphasizing its pragmatic interests was Roger W. Bolz, former Editor-in-Chief of *Automation Magazine,* and now a well-known consultant on automation planning and application.

Equally distinguished are the chairmen of the four panels in the subject areas around which the symposium was organized. Chairing the section on technology was William R. Hough, vice president for Research, Development and Engineering of Reliance Electric Company, co-sponsors of the symposium. For the panel on education the chairman was Ralph W. Tyler, Director Emeritus of the Center for Advanced Study in the Behavioral Sciences and now Senior Advisor, Science Research Associates, a subsidiary of International Business Machines Corp. Heading the panel on social organization was Dr. Robert Dubin, a Senior Fulbright Research Fellow in England, and Professor at the University of California in Irvine. Our own Dr. Howard R. Smith, Head of the Management Department in the College of Business Administration at the University of Georgia, chaired the panel on business and the economy.

The stage for all discussions at the symposium was set by position papers prepared and distributed in advance to all participants. Clifford E. Evanson, president of TAB Engineers, Inc., of Chicago, who is well known for his contributions to the literature and data of automation evaluation and planning, wrote the paper on technology. In the subject area of education, the author was Dr. Grant Venn, who is Associate Commissioner for Adult, Vocational and Library Programs in the United States Office of Education. Dr. Herbert S. Kleiman, senior economist with Battelle Memorial Institute in Columbus, Ohio, developed the position statements for panels on business and the economy. A position paper on the social cultural dimensions of automation was prepared by the University of Georgia's Dr. Fredrick L. Bates, Head of the Department of Sociology and Anthropology. These stimulating papers and discussions are included in this volume.

Basis for Future Symposia

In sense the symposium did not resolve any issues, but it did identify and clarify many of them. It sets the stage for further evaluation of questions of vital concern in our society and provides a proven means of addressing these problems. It establishes a basis for participation in future symposia which in turn builds a base for charting the course of this technology and assessing its social implications. The symposium also establishes the groundwork for an expanded program of activities at the University of Georgia focused on the area of automation and society.

In the current symposium, in future symposia, and in an

enlarged program of automation and society projects, the University of Georgia expects to:

1. Address automation per se as a salient factor in the elemental requirement to produce goods and services.
2. Examine how automation in the production of goods and services affects and is affected by other aspects of the economy, education, government, and social organization.
3. Focus on automation's impact through the expression of informed opinions, delineation of scientific fact, wide experience and varied knowledge rather than to strive (solely) for some kind of consensus.
4. Stimulate an audience beyond the University through various media by capitalizing on a clear definition of the subject material, the knowledge of the participants in our programs, the candid quality of their participation, the diversity of their backgrounds, and the currency of their information.

It seems particularly appropriate that this first Symposium on Automation and Society, a subject so portentous in terms of its future implications, should be held on the campus of America's oldest state-chartered University. The Charter of 1785 defined the University's mission "to teach and to inquire into the nature of things." Over the years the University of Georgia, conscious of its historic past, has maintained its continuity through dedication to these historic principles. With each generation the mission has been reinterpreted and extensively applied to many areas of inquiry.

Instruction, research, and public services define our contemporary roles. The University, as other institutions in our society, has been and will be profoundly affected by rapidly changing technology. Our interest in automation and its social implications, therefore, encompasses our own internal concerns as well as those of the society which constitutes the environment in which we function.

The University of Georgia was pleased to sponsor, in association with Reliance Electric Company of Cleveland, Ohio, this first annual Symposium on Automation and Society. As an area of vital concern where the instructional, research, and service capabilities of the University are highly relevant, automation and society intrigues us. The symposium, and associated activities also provide the means for bringing together resources which can be focused upon inquiry into automation and society. The multi-disciplinary nature of these questions has brought together scholars from many academic departments as well as the support and service agencies of the University. This catalytic action has an invigorating effect on our own staff as manifest by their enthusiastic participation. A further source of gratification for us is the opportunity provided by the symposium for extending further our network of competence to academicians throughout the country and ultimately, as events unfold, throughout the world. The symposium serves as a new configuration linking together scholars with shared interests. Soon we anticipate that the symposium will serve as the hub for a network of involved experts who are in reciprocal communication on a continuing basis. Individual members of such a network serve as links to other related networks providing a complex for effective communications on vital matters of common interest.

Working Relationships Established

The added value of this symposium from our perspective is the structuring of new and more productive relationships with industry as well as with government agencies in areas of public concern. The working relationships established during the symposium planning sessions, in author's meetings and among the panel chairmen was exemplary, reflecting complementary skills and experiences. This was a "shirtsleeve" arrangement. There was a full commitment by all parties involved. We anticipate that relationships of this kind will proliferate to further enhance our resources. The mix of scholars, practitioners, managers, communicators — drawn from education, industry, government, and other institutions for this symposium — had an invigorating effect on all.

This volume is a result of this first symposium. The areas defined, issues revealed, the scope of the subject provide a foundation for future inquiry so that hopefully man's control of technology from a humanistic perspective can be enhanced. As J.C. Keebler, Editor of *Automation,* commented in the April 1969 issue — "Let us elect any course except ignorance."

2

The Challenge of Automation

Hugh D. Luke

Hugh D. Luke, President, Reliance Electric Company, Cleveland, earned his BSCE at the University of Cincinnati. Joining Reliance in 1953 he subsequently became vice president of group operations: a member of the board of directors; vice president-operations, responsible for all United States operations; and executive vice president. He was appointed president in 1965. Mr. Luke is a director of The Cleveland Trust Company, The Illuminating Company and Parker-Hannifin Corporation, is on the executive committee of Machinery & Allied Products Institute, is president of the Greater Cleveland YMCA and is president and a trustee of educational television station WVIZ in Cleveland.

Never before has American industry felt such a tremendous need to increase its product output and quality. It is challenged by both domestic and overseas competition, pressured by governmental agencies acting on behalf of the user, and taken to task by the user himself who not only expects, but demands increasing product quality and safety without commensurate price increases.

These pressures are forcing industry to search for solutions, and the answer with increasing frequency is a greater application of automation.

Automation is also proving itself as the answer to internal industrial labor problems. It is one of industry's best offenses against the rising cost of labor. In the coming decade, industry will look to automation to help alleviate the growing problem of lack of adequate labor. This problem is already evident in many geographical areas of the country, especially within skilled and semi-skilled labor categories. Compounding the labor problem is the limited physical ability of man to produce sufficient volume and quality to meet the needs of our exploding population.

Modern industry has an ever-increasing sociological involvement. Historically, the growth of industry and the rise of our nation's standard of living have gone hand in hand. Now, this sociological relationship extends beyond material possessions and into pressing social areas that include education, pollution of our environment and the judicious utilization of our threatened resources.

Two Major Objectives

The importance of automation to our society prompted this first annual symposium. Two objectives were chosen as appropriate to the scope of the symposium and the knowledge of those authorities invited to participate. First, the relationship between automation and society was to be clearly defined. Second, the real problems of applying automation were to be studied, rather than the imagined problems that have caused major social groups to view automation with intense, but unjustified, apprehension.

The second objective was more easily reached than the first, but it contributed to a better understanding of the first. Concerning the real problems of automation, the symposium revealed:

1. The technology of automation is readily available but a combination of economic factors and the natural human resistance to change have impeded its application in many areas where it can be beneficial.

2. Automation must be carefully studied, planned, applied and controlled, which for the most part have not been done in the past.

It is this second revelation concerning automation that is the more volatile, both economically and socially. Industry, as it applies automation to improve the production of goods and services, must be ever aware of the way automation serves people's needs. It must study the effects of automation's leverage on the economy, on education, on the further development of technology, and on society as a whole.

Because automation exerts an influence on areas outside of

industry, it is only right that groups outside industry also be actively aware of the ways in which automation can tip the balance of our society. These groups which spring from educational, government and consumer organizations have both the time and the communications channels available to make their opinions loudly heard.

But the social action of automated industry should not result from external pressure groups. It should grow from within industry itself, simply because automation is a *unique* industrial technology. Industry must utilize automation technology to meet society's demand for goods.

Continuing Flow of Information Needed

This framework of thought guided the symposium through its sessions and to its conclusion. It is to be hoped that the problems revealed by this First Annual Symposium on Automation and Society will encourage industry to increase its understanding of the implications of automation, establish a continuing relationship within itself for the free flow of information, and act with educational, governmental and consumer groups to solve, rather than compound, society's problems through automation.

3

Automation – A Response and a Sponsor of Change

Theodore A. Smith

Theodore A. Smith, Executive Vice President, Radio Corporation of America, earned his degree in Engineering at Stevens Institute of Technology. A Fellow of the Institute of Electrical and Electronic Engineers, Mr. Smith worked on television in its early years, then on the electron microscope and in electronic data processing. He has managed RCA's operations in industrial electronics, defense, EDP and corporate planning.

We have had machines to to men's work for a long time, but always under the hand of man. The new thing which automation brings is that for some interval machines can function without direct human control. For the most part we think of automation as "the technique, method or system of operating a process without direct human intervention" — from the linking together of automatic machines to the more sophisticated systems under computer control.

There is, of course, only a thin line separating highly mechanized systems from true automation. If we tend to think of both as automation no great harm will be done, yet philosophically there may be a major point of demarcation. It appears to many that such an automation system is no longer an extension of man's faculties — that it has become a creature capable of enduring independently of man and possessing its own special attributes — including intelligence — a quality up till now reserved for man alone. Does not this lead to the conclusion that automation has usurped the qualities of man and that man, in turn, has abdicated his unique heritage to the machine?

Such a conclusion is, of course, based on many fallacies. Automation systems may operate for various periods of time without human intervention, but they are not independent of men. Men must design the systems, start them going and keep them in running order. Men must decide when and how automation is to function and must support the larger enterprise system of which automation forms only one element. The automated oil refineries could not function if it were not for the thousands of human operated filling stations which dispense their product.

Automation is Man's Servant

Automation is both dependent upon men and linked to the destiny of men. It is the product of economic, social, political and technological forces which have been taking shape for hundreds of years but which are now moving with ever increasing speed. In turn, in the years to come, it will exert its influence on the systems which compose our civilization.

The roots of automation extend back into the distant past. One of man's earliest needs was to irrigate crops. So, he invented a variety of automatic devices to pump water to a higher level, such as water wheels, windmills, or more recently, hydraulic rams, all of which can function for long periods without human attention.

During the Renaissance, men began to be deeply interested in machines and some began to think of automation. In 1546, Agricola designed an automatic gold refining system which, among other things, provided for a flow of materials from one processing station to another. Still later, we had a variety of weaving devices, of which the Jacquard loom was an advanced step in providing variable programming.

In spite of many attempts to use automation, it has progressed rather slowly. At first there were only a few simple steps in a manufacturing operation which could be automated. Even now, most manufacturing consists of some automated elements and many which are not.   Only recently has it become possible to automate complete processes.

There are many reasons for the gradual impact of automation. Fundamentally it is a system function. To be successful, all of the elements of the system must be compatible. Further, the environment in which automation can be used effectively is a critical one and is subject to a number of constraints.

For example, a certain degree of market stability is required and there must be sufficient volume of work to justify using automation. Thus, until there were enough automobiles to use gasoline and to furnish some constancy of demand, automated refineries could not be justified.

Economic Realities Predominate

Automation must be an economic element of the industrial system. It must pay off. It must be capable of being used with available materials and components. It must fit the nature of the business so that if, for example, product changes are required, the production machinery can accommodate them. This factor has led to the important development of variable automation systems subject to a greater degree of external control than the fixed systems used at first.

If a process is to be automated, there must be detailed quantitative knowledge of how the process functions. We have been surprised to find that much of our process knowledge is empirical and intuitive rather than scientific. One of my associates says that many processes depend upon intangible quantities, which he calls "goofer dust." Machines can't operate on "goofer dust."

While it is possible to automate many processes, there are some where cost is so great that automation does not pay off. In addition, steps in some conventional processes do not lend themselves to automation and it may be necessary to devise entirely new methods. In the field of electronics, one of the major costs in building large and complex equipments is the interconnection of elements. In the past, hand soldering of wires to terminals was the method used. Now an automated system under computer control is employed, but it was necessary to develop a new method of "wire wrap" as a substitute for soldering.

It is fundamental that technology be developed to a high degree both to make automation practicable and to be certain that it will perform reliably. Unreliable automation is worse than useless.

We have had to develop special instrumentation to measure the parameters of a process and to supply information in such a form that machines could act upon it.

And not least important, we have required a financial system capable of supplying funds for the acquisition of automation equipment.

Climate Must Be Favorable

Thus the environment must be favorable for the use of automation and all of the elements of the automation system must be developed to a compatible state. It has taken time to do so.

We can consider automating any of the various functions in a business enterprise. Initially most of the thrust of automation was devoted to the production elements. In recent years, we have begun to automate the information handling elements of business by means of data processing systems, and we are making a start in linking together the information and production systems. At the same time, computers have been used to automate many functions of enterprises such as banking and insurance, which do not involve physical processes. We have had a desperate need to do so since, as these institutions have grown, they have been threatened with a chaos of paperwork.

Why Use Automation?

Very obviously business applies automation to increase profits and to gain a competitive advantage. In some instances, industry has been faced with the choice of automating or perishing. One of the most current and pressing reasons to use automation has been to permit free world trade under circumstances of economic imbalance between countries in various stages of industrial development. Products produced in countries where wages are low can often be shipped and sold at very low prices in more developed nations. If industry in the developed nation is to survive, it must turn to some method for balancing the inequity of labor rates.

In the electronics industry, small radios involve a substantial amount of handwork. The most recent estimate is that about 82% of all radios sold domestically in 1968 were made abroad. Presently, we do not have an economic method for automating radio production.

There is sometimes a very compelling reason to use automation to reduce costs, which, expressed very simply, is to avoid being priced out of the market by inflationary increases. But cost is not the only reason for using automation. Our products have become more complex and sophisticated and it has been necessary to provide for automatic methods to assure uniformity and reliability. Many problems relating to product quality are the result of human failures.

Automation has also been used by industry to replace tasks which are demeaning or unworthy of human effort or so difficult to undertake that few people wish to perform them. Our company markets an automatic device to perform color corrections for printing plates. It has become increasingly difficult to find people willing to scrape away tiny elements of metal, hour after hour, in accordance with older methods of correcting plates.

Although the manufacturing industry has only begun to use automation on a rather limited scale, already there have been violent cries of alarm on the part of some who see in it a threat and a danger to all mankind. This is not, of course, a new situation. For hundreds of years some have looked upon machines as the rivals of men, taking over men's functions and depriving them of work, yet devoid of the moral qualities which men could offer.

Fear Relate to Change

There have been a number of fears voiced with respect to automation. It has been widely claimed that automation has resulted in large scale unemployment. It is said that automation has reduced the number of unskilled job opportunities so that those without superior education can no longer find work. There are other more speculative accusations.

There are, I think, two different bases for the fears of automation. The first is fear of change itself. There is a very human tendency to equate tradition with truth and goodness, and any change in tradition with evil motives.

The second fear associated with automation is fear of the unknown. The fear is based upon emotion rather than upon facts, and it has led to the involvement of automation as a whipping boy for more mundane causes of change. There are thousands of changes which have altered our lives during the last 75 years. Yet, in spite of reduction in employment in some areas, total employment has increased at a higher rate than the growth in population. Between 1890 and 1965 our population increased 3.1 times. During the same interval, total employment increased 3.4 times.

There has been a substantial increase in the number of service workers in our economy. Some have claimed that this is a phenomenon of automation in displacing blue collar workers. It is likely that mechanization and, to some degree, automation have been an underlying cause, but not for the reasons named. Mechanization and automation, by increasing productivity and by raising the standard of living, have made it possible for the public to afford and to demand many services — commercial, social, educational and medical — which previously were not feasible. Automation may be an important contributor to future social progress by making it possible for us to afford other new and beneficial public services.

Support Function Necessary
Another claim is that automation will eliminate all jobs except highly technical and scientific ones requiring a superior education. Yet automation requires many support functions — machine shop, maintenance, clerical, sales, personnel, shipping and the like. These are largely semi-skilled jobs and industry has been able to train people to undertake them. It has even been possible to teach computer programming to people without college educations.

The telephone system may be the most highly automated system in all industry and can, perhaps, illustrate what may happen when a high degree of automation has been attained. Although the cost of most services has risen, the charge for long distance calls, which involved a substantial amount of manual switching cost in 1920, have been sharply reduced. A transcontinental call cost $16.50 in 1920. The price is currently $1.75 and less than half this value late at night. During this same period, the use of telephones increased from about 9 million in 1920 to 83 million in 1967. Overall, the Bell

System operations had some 656,000 employees in 1967, not including research and manufacturing, which is about three times the number in 1920. During the period of automation, wages increased substantially. For example, between 1954 and 1966, the average increase in employee earnings was 59%.

Neither the variety of services nor the expansion of the telephone network would have been possible had it not been for developments in technology and the use of automation. And much of the expansion of the telephone system has been due to increased demand resulting from the higher standard of living brought about by mechanization and automation.

Thus, automation is both a response to change as well as a sponsor of change.

4

A Look at
Automation and Technology

C. English Evanson

C. English Evanson, President, TAB Engineers, is a registered professional engineer and earned his degree from the Illinois Institute of Technology. He received *Automation* magazine's Citation of Honor in recognition of his contribution to the fund of practical knowledge on the technology of automation at the First Conference on Manufacturing Automation at Purdue University. Mr. Evanson is a consultant in the designing and building of automated production systems, recognized in particular for his contributions to the literature and data on automation evaluation and planning.

Automation has been defined in many ways. At times it has been described as no more than another word for mechanization, at other times it has been defined very broadly, and sometimes it has been limited to controls and computers. For the purposes of this paper we shall assume a rather broad all-encompassing viewpoint in our discussion of automation so as to include the public domain as well as the industrial processes. We shall, however, exclude the military and space research areas.

The Tool Engineers Handbook[1] offers a preliminary insight into the area in which we are interested with this comment:

"Automation may be defined for the industrial area as the application of machinery to perform and control automatically and continuously all the manufacturing operations in a given plant, from the raw material to the finished product. In its optimum development, automation embraces the most complete, feasible mechanization of the individual handling, machining or processing, inspecting, assembling, testing, packaging, and programming operations, plus the integration of all equipment and operations for continuous mutual coordination, regulation, adjustment, correction, and control. The primary objectives of automation are: 1. Balanced and controlled production; 2. Uniform and controlled quality; and 3. Lower manufacturing costs."

---

1. References are listed at close of chapter.

By substituting a few words we can revise this definition so that it applies to the public domain as well. Thus, automation may also be defined as the application of machinery to perform and control automatically and continually all the operations in a given public service area. In its optimum development, it embraces the most complete, feasible mechanization of the handling, processing, transporting and programming operations, plus the integration of all equipment and operations for continuous mutual coordination, regulation, adjustment, correction and control. The primary objectives of automation in this public sector are: 1. Balanced and controlled operation; 2. Uniform and controlled performance; and 3. Promotion of the public welfare (maximum availability of public services at minimum cost).

Applicable Definitions

An erudite and rather comprehensive definition of automation is to be found in *The Encyclopedia Americana*[2] . Since it concerns itself with the broad social, as well as technological effects of automation, this definition is particularly applicable to this Symposium:

"Automation, an advanced technique of industrial manufacturing and scientific investigation which has evolved from the basic concepts of the machine and mass production. Hence, automation represents a new level in the continuing industrial revolution. Because of the power of automation to formalize and to expedite scientific thought production, the consequences of this new technique will have a more profound effect on our civilization than the mere development of a new technique of manufacture. In effect, automation is promoting a technological revolution which dwarfs, in significance, the concurrent industrial revolution . . .

"The difference between automation and mass production

lies in the complete integration of fully automatic machines without the need for man as an intermediary. The machines are self-loading and self-unloading with conveyors guiding the goods in various stages of production from machine to machine. Electronic controls and actuators coordinate the functions of the various machines even to the point of correcting for errors and evaluating the quality of the finished products. Hence, from new material to finished product the entire manufacturing process is automatic without the intervention of man. The automatic controls are capable of making swift decisions when confronted with a predetermined set of variables in a variety of possible patterns. Materials, such as radio-active substances, which cannot be used in normal manufacturing processes because of the hazard to human life can be used in the automatic factory without peril.

"The fully automatic factory has not yet been achieved at the production level. However, there are semiautomatic factories in existence as well as a large variety of fully automatic machines which consummate a particular group of manufacturing operations . . ."

Automation Trends

Reference to the "state of the art" in this discussion will apply primarily to the knowledge and hardware now available to transport, process, control and distribute the various goods and services in our economy. Transport will include the movement of raw materials, finished goods, and the necessary catalyst, people. Control will include the sensors, the logic and commands, and the reporting.

In looking ahead it is useful to examine some of the breakthroughs emerging from the world's laboratories. The new technology purview includes new processing and control methods and, as well, new materials. We cannot neglect, of course, the impact of the future generations of computers and of the new power sources which will become available.

No discussion of this nature would be realistic without recognizing that application always lags the art considerably. How and why it lags, of course, is determined mainly by its economic payoff. Much of the art is still very expensive when compared with the cost of comparable human effort. Thus, trends by industry differ widely — some already have an appreciable degree of automation; some we can expect to see growing actively in the future, for example, in construction; some new industries will adopt automation directly without passing through the evolutionary equipment growth of the older industries as well it may be with ocean farming. In the public domain changes can be expected in transportation, water waste recycling, communications and the wide proliferation of computers throughout business, government, education and even into our homes. The medical field and the need for the control of pollution will also be burgeoning areas of automation.

The future will require a change in the factors for determining the degree of application of automation. Now the major factor is economic payback. In the future, especially in the public domain, human needs and comfort and the welfare of the human race will have to predominate especially in reducing and controlling air pollution, water pollution, noise disturbances, medical efforts, transportation problems, and public safety hazards.

A Look at Technology

While each observer may and perhaps does have his own concept of automation, with no two being exactly alike, yet all being similar, it is evident that we would belabor the point to try to find a common denominator to suit everyone. For this reason it is most practical to assume the broad systems implication of automation as it applies to any useful work in industry, in the household, transportation, medicine, and agriculture. Because of their unique and specialized character, it is not reasonable to include military automation nor space exploration automation.

The key word in the preceding paragraph was system. As it is applied, the term can refer to a department, a single production line, a single plant, or it may involve a large network such as a telephone or electrical service network. Without a knowledge of what the system is, what it is supposed to do, what influences act upon it and how the system is affected by these influences there can be little hope for a successful automation program.

One of the major reasons for failure in some attempts at automation in the earlier days (and even today yet) resulted from not recognizing this fact. It was assumed by many that any engineer with good credentials in a recognized discipline could successfully head an automation program. Similarly companies that had supplied a satisfactory line of equipment for many years, thought that merely by so deciding they could become automation specialists.

This simply is not possible for most companies. Automation technology integrates all of the engineering disciplines and, in addition, includes some that are not engineering. The automation engineer (the word engineer is used for lack of a better term: other terms could be expert, leader, specialist, manager, etc.) must use a total system approach to an automation project. He must be able to see the overall scope of any project in its entirety and yet be able to refocus on critical details within a discipline. He does not need to be an expert in any contributing discipline, but he must be able to interpret and relate the outputs or needs of one discipline with another and must be able to interpret or communicate these to management.

In the broad sense which we are using to describe automation in this paper, "management" may be the management of an individual company, an individual plant, a government bureau, or of a municipality (the town fathers). The automation specialist must also understand economics and the humanistic impacts of the project which affect the workers, guide the designers, limit the builders of the equipment, influence the people who are to operate and maintain it and, of course, satisfy management. Such a paragon perhaps does not exist or if one were found, he would probably be lured into other more lucrative fields.

As said before, the importance of the system concept was not fully realized when automation was in its early stages. However, more and more people have recognized this fact especially with the growth in size and complexity of programs until today we see many firms joint venturing their talents under a single head to complete difficult projects.

For example, it was once thought that to acquire a successful automated or even a fully mechanized warehouse one had only to call a conveyor company. Even the conveyor companies now know that the necessary sophisticated controls and computer system logic require their joining forces with others who have developed and refined these special talents.

Continuing on this subject of how general attitudes have changed in the past twenty years, most management people have changed their viewpoint. During the 40's and 50's, except for a few enlightened management teams, managers chose to view automation as simply a better type of machine tool or another faster piece of office equipment. They chose not to listen to anyone who explained the critical need to fit the product and the automation system together, especially if it meant modifying the product. Similarly, in the case of office automation, many could see no need to modify their current paper procedures in order to achieve the best results with the new equipment being purchased. The consequences were some horrible examples in the shop and some very costly false-starts in the office.

Today many more managements understand the need to integrate their product design with their automation plans. In fact, many companies have put Value Engineering groups into their design departments to get the benefits of such integration as quickly as possible. Thus we see that in the twenty years that automation has been an accepted technology, management appreciation and understanding of automation and its requirements has grown appreciably. The pioneer contributors to the field of automation literature deserve our thanks for this improvement in the business environment.

State of the Art

It is generally agreed that the word automation was first used officially in 1946 although the activity for which it stood had been developing for some time. The exigencies of World War II had forced the technological development with new scientific breakthroughs and new production techniques emerging as a result. The post-war conversion from a military to a consumer oriented economy required a great deal of re-tooling.

A significant change in the labor pool for peace-time products had occurred. Wage rates had doubled and redoubled. Even at the increased wage rates there was a shortage of labor available to supply the pent-up demand for goods made by pre-war methods. Faster and cheaper means of production had to be found. To accomplish this the new war-time techniques and discoveries were brought into use by the engineers of production and automation was well on its way into the modern scene!

In the twenty some years that the word automation has been with us many more new engineering and scientific developments have taken place. The magnetic wire recorder of World War II developed into the magnetic tape decks and memories we know and use today.

The proponents of analog and digital computing systems argued the relative merits of each for control of processes and machining. Digital won out for machining and developed into the numerical control methods while analog generally was accepted as preferable for certain kinds of processing operations.

Airborne electronic equipment had forced the development of the smaller vacuum tubes and industry was adjusting to these changes when the transistor was invented in 1948. This, within a few years ushered in the era of solid-state circuitry. Whereas limitations as to size of computers had been forecast because of the heat generated by the many vacuum tubes, now the computers could be larger in function and smaller in physical size with little problem of heat.

Computer Use Expanding

The proliferation of computer models, the desire for flexibility, the constant search for reduced size led eventually to the integrated circuit. When the production of integrated circuits reaches an acceptable level of quality control by normal industrial standards, another cost breakthrough in computers will be realized. For practical purposes we can say computers have been available for only about twenty years, one human generation, yet the computer of today is the great grandson of the early models of twenty years ago. Likewise, application of computers is now limited only by the imagination and resources of the owner and user. Computers are used to read and command other sub-system computers. Computers can now by-pass the necessity of producing tapes for N/C machines by controlling the machines directly. Time-sharing has brought powerful computers and programs within the reach of all. The field is so dynamic that to say "this is the status" is to be wrong tomorrow.

Twenty years ago the laser and maser were no more than the imagination of a science fiction writer. Today lasers are used for certain machining operations, to balance rotors, measure distances and accurately guide tunneling machines underground. And as an indication of how fast technology is moving, computerized microwave and modulated light surveying equipment had just begun to replace the standard transit on our far-flung highway program when the laser transit and its greater accuracy made its entree and impact into the surveying field. Although the principles of light interference have been known for a long time, it was not until 1956 that the science of holography was founded. Now we have three-dimensional printing and research is proceeding in the attempt to utilize the theories of holography to produce three-dimensional television.

Television was in its infancy twenty years ago and made its first mild impact about the same time the term automation did. But it was a few more years before industry was able to receive the benefits of closed-circuit television. Now cameras have become small enough and versatile enough to allow them to be used in such otherwise inaccessible places as the inside of a clogged sewer pipe. In combination with remote controls, television cameras allow workers to get "close" to see and manipulate an otherwise too dangerous operation. What started out as an interesting toy has become an indispensable part of the control system in many plants.

The staggering impact of these examples is really how

short the lead-time has become for a theory to emerge from the laboratory as working technology and be installed for practical use. Before the age of automation, it usually required about twenty years for a theory to be put to any productive work in industry. This length of time is now decreasing to a few years. The critical implication of this is that if one has a three-year program under development it could be partly or completely obsolete by the time the project is installed. However, a more realistic reaction is to recognize that change is with us and to constantly maintain review points both during the project and after it is installed.

Not with us twenty years ago or in their extreme infancy were some of our controls. Proximity switches were limited to photocells, pyrometers and some magnetic switches. These have been markedly improved in speed of response and accuracy. And, added to these are the capacitive switch, the inductive switch the infrared detector, the sonic switch and the air switch. These can detect the presence or position of an object from .001" to several inches away.

Just as semiconductors and solid-state circuitry solved some of the environmental problems of electronic circuit applications, so now fluidics (pneumatic logic) allows equivalent logic circuits to be placed in magnetic and electric field and in vibrational or explosive areas impractical for electronic circuitry.

Along with the improvement of components has developed the knowledge and sophistication of the circuitry. Feedback "hunting" is now minimal and a great deal of the available circuitry is off-the-shelf. Importantly, this circuitry can also produce a running record of the system's performance in the form of charts or when combined with other inputs it can generate totals on volume, costs, degree of quality performance, etc.

Influence of Materials

At the same time that many of the elements of automation have become more sophisticated, many of the raw materials have changed considerably also. Most notable has been the veritable explosion of plastics with their manifold properties. These have greatly assisted designers in discovering simpler methods of achieving finishes, part simplification, structural strength, and automatic assembly and packaging.

Similarly, papers today have many properties undreamed of a generation ago. The same can be said for glass and ceramics which have made new inroads on the construction field especially. The metals fields, both ferrous and non-ferrous have not been idle. New alloys, new combinations, new shapes, the expanded choices in powdered metals, have given the designer new dimensions to his thinking. In fact, the difficult problem many times is not "What will do it?," but rather, "Which will do it at the best value?"

Lubricants are a good example of the very broad scope of properties now available in today's materials — for every temperature, environment, condition and expected life of the equipment. Maintenance of equipment has been assisted also by plug-in components and sub-assemblies. This has speeded up emergency repair to the point where it has obviated the need in many cases for expensive standby equipment and overly large in-process "float" storage.

New Processes

Several new processes have been developed within industry these same twenty years all of which have had a marked influence on the economy. One of the most dramatic has been the freezing of fresh and cooked foods. Actually, a whole new industry has developed as a result. An added boost has been the introduction of Cryogenics to the industry. It is now one of the important parts of the field. It is particularly critically important for the fishing industry and for pulpy food items such as tomatoes and strawberries because conventional freezing is so slow that as the water in the product freezes and expands, the cellular structures rupture. Then upon thawing the product becomes mushy. With the faster cryogenic freezing this undesirable characteristic is minimized.

While on the subject of frozen foods we should mention the relatively recent freeze-dry process where the boiling point for the water in the frozen product is reduced by evacuating the surrounding area. This allows the water (as ice) to sublimate without the natural oils and flavors also doing so.

Dielectric heating has been known and used for many years, but the use of microwave energy is a rather late outgrowth of the radar of World War II. Microwave energy can be used to cut processing times from hours to minutes. As knowledge about its uses and control become more widely disseminated it will have greater and greater impact on industry where quick drying or heating is required.

In the metals field the new processes of electrical discharge machining, electrochemical machining and electron beam machining have been added. They have been called exotic methods, but they are economically sound when properly used. Similarly, laser welding of ultra-small parts, ultrasonic cleaning, welding and inspection and electromagnetic forming and friction welding are all new processes that will become less dramatic as they are utilized more fully.

Numerical Control

By far the greatest change in the machine shop has been N/C, numerical control of machining. From its tentative beginnings as a play-back recording system for a tracer lathe to today's fully equipped N/C job shop is a dramatic chapter in the annals of the machine tool industry. Familiarity and progress with N/C equipment has proceeded to the point where practically any degree of sophistication is attainable. Hardware and peripheral software are available to combine a number of N/C units into a processing complex with automatic process planning, throughput control, inspection and accounting.

The field of materials handling has probably benefitted more from the growth of automation than any other field. This is only natural because the results in this field are so self-evident. While most of the great variety of transport means were available twenty years ago, they were seldom integrated with equipment as a system in those days. Furthermore, many items such as turnovers, while procurable, were not off-the-shelf items. This integration with equipment, the increase in standard units and the development of controlled conveying systems are the most marked advancements in the materials handling field. It is difficult to find a picture of an "automated area" which does not have at least some conveyors in it. Consequently, in many peoples' minds, the automatic transport of materials has become synonomous with automation.

Materials handling continued its development outside the plant with new uses for pipelines such as slurries to move granular substances. Overland conveyors many miles long have been designed to move excavated material, construction material, coal and fill.

And all too few conveyors for people have been developed and installed.

In addition to the "evolution" there have also been some notable innovations and advancements during those years. The transfer machine, although based on older proved machine design principles, became an industry standard.

Vibratory bowls developed from an experimental curiosity

to involved sophisticated cascades of storage, cleaning and feeding units.

Magnetic belts were developed to separate ferrous items, then to convey and finally to also carry magnetic instructions along with the loads.

Floor carts became radio controlled or electronically controlled with wires in the floor.

With industry's acceptance of pallets a whole field of loaders, stackers, and line storage equipment has been developed. Loading and unloading conveyors have been installed in truck bodies and the air glide has been developed to allow a man to easily move a one-ton pallet load.

As machining speeds increased in the shop, the removal of chips necessitated the development of chip removal systems.

The changes and advances being made in controls, processes, equipment and material are constantly continuing. It is natural to wonder what tomorrow's breakthrough will be. Having a few inventions to his credit, the writer knows how difficult it is to create something and then how simple it appears to others after it's been done the first time. And such is the case here, to name what is next on the horizon is just about equivalent to inventing it.

State of Application

It would indeed be presumptious for one to attempt to determine the degree of application of automation in industry. Therefore, I will attempt to give some examples in the various fields of work and from these try to arrive at some conclusions.

We've seen from the previous comments that in twenty years since automation was first named there has been a revolution in the means available for accomplishing production. Also the manufacturing processes themselves have undergone a mild revolution during this time. Thus, it would be safe to say that a company making anything the same way it made it ten or more years ago is probably doing it inefficiently by today's standards.

In the field of mining this period saw the development of boring machines and conveying equipment that will enter a mine, dig and convey the raw minerals to the surface. Two factors stand in the way of fully automatic mining, especially in coal mines. One is the owner's concern for cost and the second is the miner's fear for their jobs.

A current pilot operation, however, is testing the application of remote control of automatic mining machines. They are self-propelled into horizontal shafts and controlled and guided by control consoles outside the shafts. So far these have worked reasonably well except where the veins fluctuate appreciably.

Actually, the mining in itself is no longer the major production problem. The major problem is getting the product out of the tunnel as quickly as it is mined or cut and to keep the equipment running full time.

A major source of raw materials is agriculture. And here automation truly has upset the pattern of living probably more than in any other single segment of our economy. Single family farms of years ago are becoming a thing of the past. An appreciable number of today's farms are large corporations run by professional managers, many with advanced degrees in their specialties. The farm workers no longer are wise only in the ways of growing crops, but also are wise in the ways of equipment. They are, in fact, proficient mechanics.

Mechanization and automation in agriculture has proceeded step with step with the laboratories. The search for better seed, more uniform growth and ripening patterns, indeed, the development of growth patterns to suit machines have materially aided the conversion from hand labor to machinery. Just as a factory will go on two or three shifts to meet high-production seasonal demand, so too does the modern crop "factory" operate around the clock during critical periods of planting and harvesting. A good classic example of farm automation is the wheat combine which cuts the wheat, thrashes it, bales the straw and delivers the grain to accompanying trucks.

To gather those items which cannot be automatically harvested, workers (40 to 80) are carried across a field while lying above a conveyor belt. In this system a giant tractor pulls two outrigger conveyors while the workers cut or pick the product and drop it onto the conveyors which carry the product to the tractor and thence to following trucks. Thus, even where automation is not yet possible, mechanization is used widely. An interesting example of modern farming is an air-conditioned chicken house with individual coops for the hens, piped and timed water and feed, conveyed droppings and conveyed eggs, automatically cleaned conveyor belts, and automatically timed lighting system.

In discussing agriculture we should perhaps mention two other trends — one, the constant shrinkage of the citrus groves and the other, the still not fully-automatic milk production system. At the rate in which land is being gobbled up for housing developments, industrial tracts and recreational facilities, the time will come when citrus juice production will be fully automated and completely synthetic. Similarly, although milk handling is almost completely automatic from udder to package and the cows automatically fed, the barns semi-automatically cleaned, nonetheless the care and comfort of the contented cow requires many valuable acres of ground and many man hours of labor. Research is therefore under way to determine how to produce milk synthetically in a factory. It is probable that within the next decade synthetic milk will be on the store shelves.

From the mines and farms the materials go to the refineries, mills, canneries and factories.

Some of the best examples of automation are to be found in the refineries whose product lends itself to continuous programming and control. Steel making has with its continuous casting, and automatic computer controlled rolling mills leaped upward in the scale of automation also.

Canneries whose line speeds have risen from sixty and a hundred cans a minute to the neighborhood of a thousand a minute can be categorized as in the upper half of industry's automation scale. More and more of the operations of cleaning, inspecting, cutting, and cooking are becoming continuous and fully automatic. Seasonal peaks and valleys are limiting economic factors to the greater use of automation.

The thousands of fabricating plants that convert the many materials into millions of products make an evaluation of the status of automation application in the general manufacturing area an almost impossible task. It depends upon the product, the size of the company, the volume produced, the progressiveness of the company's management and the ingenuity of the engineers.

Areas Least Automated

Generally, speaking, and recognizing that there are thousands of products made by thousands of different companies, the assembly, final test and warehousing are probably the least automated, on the average, in comparison with the other major operations. Assembly is least automated because of cost, complexity, and/or the frequent need to redesign the product for automatic assembling. Final testing is not automated in many cases because, surprisingly enough, many manufacturers do not really know how to test their products without destroying them. Warehousing is not as automated as it could be because of the large investment which is usually required.

The transportation and distribution of the product to the consumer is a most difficult phase for which to plan a system of automation unless a direct tie between the producer and consumer can be made. Such a tie is exemplified by the producer of cans who builds his plant adjacent to a cannery and supplies the cans by means of a conveyor through the walls of the two plants.

This, of course, is the exceptional case and it is extremely difficult to plan even a relatively small distribution network system because the system necessarily gets entangled with a multitude of other factors not under the control of the systems men of any one manufacturing company. Some of the difficulties of our distribution system — and here I'm speaking of the technical not the equity factors — is that trucks carrying products must travel the same highways which are traveled by the vacationer, the worker, and the housewife. It would make much more sense to provide a large trenched out and covered over conveying system to transport goods between major population centers than to build extra roads for extra trucks and cars.

We have found in our modern in-plant material handling systems that it is best to divorce the flow of materials from the movement of people. Yet we continue to mix both in our movement between plants and between cities.

As a hypothetical question, what would happen if we had another AT&T, say the American Tollway and Transport Company? This company would receive a franchise, as does the telephone company, and would rent all vehicles and other transporting equipment to the users on a monthly basis as the telephone company rents its equipment. It would maintain the arteries of transport, the terminals and the interchanges.

It is possible that its scope would have to include air freight, railroads, trucks, barges, conveyors, and pipelines. One can wonder what the progress of our roads (both highway and rail) would be, what the safety record would be and how soon we would have automated highways.

What I'm leading up to is that the time is past when an individual manufacturing company can attempt to decide for itself what is best on those questions and problems which affect the outside community. Today a plant is built in a new area and suddenly new traffic jams occur, old desultory intersections are suddenly dangerous, the local water table drops, a new housing development for the influx of workers overtaxes the sewer system, the school system and the local safety facilities.

T.M. Comella has commented[3] pointedly on the issue involved: "Most actions are expedient. People react to specific problems without thinking them through, propose solutions without understanding the kind of ethical values they endorse, and implement those solutions without being aware of their long-range consequences. The result of this mass reaction process is the creation of social progress without purpose, ethics or justice. Only objective values can legislate the course of a free society. Without them, the destiny of a nation – and its institutions – will be dictated by a random choice of expedient actions."

It is this "random choice of expedient actions" that we have observed up to the present, which have polluted our water, our air, offended our ears, and in too many cases offended our environment. In our automation programs of the future, we must, as part of these programs, take into consideration not only the immediate need but as well the proper return to the environment of the by-products and wastes of industry and commerce.

Automation a Blessing

In closing, the Encyclopedia Americana[2] is perhaps prophetic in terms of the major concern of this Symposium: "Automation means the ultimate divorcement of man from the machine as an integral part of its operation. This is, perhaps, the greatest blessing of automation. A society based on industrial automation should enjoy standards of material welfare and freedom which are difficult to comprehend at this time. Automation offers even to the most underprivileged parts of the world opportunities which are now almost impossible. However, there is the potential danger that man will direct a disproportionate share of his intellectual effort to the machine as the source of his bounty. There is even the danger that man will delegate to the automatic machine some of his gift of free will. To meet the challenges of the automatic age our greatest weapon is education – not education in the sense of vocational training but education for all people in the spiritual and intellectual beauties of life. In this way the automatic machine can be made a force for good and provide for all the people a measure of the good life heretofore reserved for a relatively few people. This rise of popular democracy which grew out of the industrial revolution and continues to prosper in an age of mechanized industry will continue to prosper as the only possible form of government in an automatic age . . ."

REFERENCES AND BIBLIOGRAPHY

1. *Tool Engineers Handbook*, Second Edition, American Society of Tool and Manufacturing Engineers, McGraw-Hill Book Co., 1959.

2. *The Encyclopedia Americana*, 1966 Edition.

3. "Call to Leadership," T.M. Comella, *Automation Magazine*, January 1968, The Penton Publishing Co.

4. *Anatomy of Automation,* Amber & Amber, Prentice-Hall, Inc., Englewood Cliffs, N.J., 1962.

5. *Automating the Manufacturing Process*, George F. Hawley, Reinhold Publishing Corp., New York, 1959.

6. *Automation and Technological Change*, Prentice-Hall, Inc., Englewood Cliffs, N.J., 1962.

7. *Office Work and Automation*, Howard S. Levin, John Wiley & Sons, Inc., New York, 1956.

8. *Science & Technology Magazine*, International Communications, Inc. (a subsidiary of Conover-Mast Publicaitons, Inc.) New York, various issues.

9. *Understanding Automation*, Roger W. Bolz, The Penton Publishing Co., Cleveland, Ohio 1966.

5

Technology's Reach
and the User's Grasp

Chairman:
William R. Hough

Deliberations on the Technological Aspects of Automation

William R. Hough, Vice President — Research, Development and Engineering, Reliance Electric Company, is a graduate of the University of Michigan. An innovator in a-c and d-c motors, industrial drive systems, and the application of solid state electronics to the control of industrial processes, Mr. Hough's special interests are related to technological forecasting, growth and development of automation.

In taking a serious and intense look at automation as we have defined it for the purpose of this symposium, in all probability the most outstanding fact that emerges is that the actual technology available is far more advanced than its application. And, it probably will always be so. The present level of the technology appears to be mainly that of man planning what is to be done, programming what is to be done and then automatically controlling the process according to the plan developed — but by and large in bits and pieces or in limited areas.

Application of the technology of automation using even rudimentary systems approach is limited. Total systems theory applied to really large installations is almost nonexistant. But, the one distinguishing factor about automation is its systems implication. A system of course can be bounded by any number of perimeters. We can have a solar system which includes the planets and the sun; but we can also have a system that deals with just two entities within a single production line, within a single department, or within a single plant. Again, we can enlarge our system to deal with a multiplicity of plants. Today it is becoming necessary to think in terms of systems. Until there was real understanding that the benefits of automation are derived by following a systematic approach, many efforts, especially among industrial engineers, merely created bottlenecks. In other words, automating to solve a bottleneck created another bottleneck by trying to solve the problem from too narrow a viewpoint with no concern for the implications and effects of that solution upon other factors immediately adjacent.

Limitations Are Many

As a matter of practical reality, the present applications of automation technology are definitely limited by economics. This is especially true in industry where there is an absolute need for justification of expenditures. However, there are many cases extant wherein the limitation is plainly a lack of understanding of the process itself that is to be automated.

Other situations are present that also create limitations. One is the inertia of individuals. There are such factors as social rate of change − acceptance of the new, the different. And, there is always the knowledge barrier, the rate at which new knowledge is assimilated and put to use.

In the manufacture of ball bearings, which all agree is a pretty complicated and demanding task where the variety is great, there are some companies that start out with raw materials in the form of a rod and sleeve and end up with boxes of ball bearings quality programmed to go all over the world, without any human hands touching them in between. The amazing thing about that is that it does fit the major requirements of automation − it definitely has lowered the manufacturing costs, created uniform and controlled quality, and it does lend itself to a production control. In fact, some of these ball bearing factories are probably as fully automatic as will ever be obtained. All of the aspects of inspection and quality control are done by machine. In such areas automatic factories are here and they are not as fully developed in this country as they are in some others. Japan is far more advanced in some of these areas than we and thus contributes to our import-export imbalance.

Availability and Ability Problems

In one sense it seems we are generating new information faster than we can develop ability to use it. Handling information, storing information or retrieving information has, it appears, little relationship to the ability, willingness, or time with which to create concrete results. As has been learned in the computer field at great expense, it is of no value to automatically process incorrect input data.

It is equally realistic in other areas to note the utter waste resulting from automating the wrong process, the wrong product or even merely poorly planned operations.

It is interesting to notice, in this whole technological development, the fact that you have to achieve certain technological innovations before you can move on another step. For instance, as in transportation, efforts had begun toward automating but revealed technological blockages that wouldn't allow particular aspects to move forward. There were technological requirements to be met before it was possible to move on to the next step. This appears true through all industries, even when a minor limitation is the problem.

Although technological "gaps" do create difficulties, it may even be more critical when management ignores the importance of the time factor. Most problems can be solved satisfactorily to a degree in spite of such gaps but seldom when the economic time factor has been subject to abuse.

From the personal experiences discussed at this meeting, it seems generally true that most problems are not attacked until they become really acute. Most industries seem to ignore problems, do not anticipate problems by and large, wait until the problems get relatively big, and then try to solve them themselves. Reluctantly they seek someone to solve them, and then eventually when the time table is running short, then they go for expert opinion. As one example, a company recently had to meet some orders for a new line of products and wanted to be in production within five months. Asked how they had come up with such a short lead time — it proved that 18 months had been spent in thinking about it and talking about it with various people and not looking at the total system problem until it was almost too late.

The fact is there are three main constraints in automating. One is technological, one is social, and the third is theoretical. The technological may not be the most important.

Social Constraints a Key

In spite of some technological constraints, these are far fewer than the social constraints. In construction for instance — there are equipment manufacturers who build what they call "packaged boilers." In other words, they put the whole thing in a package, you can buy it, have it shipped, and installed by just putting bolts into the foundations. Yet the codes in many cities require that when the package is delivered, that it shall be unpiped, taken down, and then repiped by the plumbers' union. The values of automation to the consumer are lost.

One of the really basic problems of technology is frequently that the people who are developing the technology do not look at the whole picture, and, as yet, there is no well-established, accepted way of looking at the whole thing.

Of course, we have to recognize that we have made a lot of progress — we may have a great many problems, but we have made a lot of progress, through technology and through the evolution of mankind, in the past 30 to 50 years. No matter what system you are considering or what problem you are considering, there is always a practical matter theorized where you concluded properly every consideration.

But, here we must differentiate between scientific investigation and invention. Even the courts have indicated that if you can develop something mathematically, it is not really an invention. The engineer by training and inclination needs two things in order that he can invent. He needs first direction — to be told what is wanted — and then he needs the where-withal — the money and the lab to do it; and, granted these, usually he can accomplish most of the things that he set out to accomplish. Now, if you can accomplish them for the amount of time and money you want — that's another factor. But most engineers are not inventive in a sense that they see that we need some particular item and create it thereupon — rather somebody else usually points out what is needed, and the engineer comes in to solve it. He's trained in school liter-ally to do it that way.

Advocates Needed

Whatever the institution that attacks a problem — be it business or university or government group or what have you — that group has to be dedicated to doing something about it or it ends up being a great theoretical exercise. There has to be the leadership and determination to analyze, to the point that that leadership judges the matter can stand analysis with-in the economic environment that exists. There has to be an advocate, also, and that advocate has got to go out and merchandise the idea — again without regard to formal organ-ization — and then you are going to get something done. As the complexity of the problem increases, the organization has to consider more factors in the creation of its system solution and you've got to go through those steps of analysis and advocacy or you are not going to get anything done. It may not be perfect, but life isn't perfect and it seems that we are making a lot of progress, as imperfect as we may be.

Many small businesses — with just a few million dollars in

gross sales — do not feel that automation is for them. On the other hand, a case in point was a manufacturer of a high-quality candy whose sales were about one and a half million dollars, and who wasn't able to fill his orders. By giving him a new process — a continuous process — that was a new system from the handling of the nuts and the syrup right at the beginning through to the packaging, he didn't have to build a new building, and was able to cut his production staff where the automatic process was handled by two people instead of about 15 he had before. Now there was a displacement of workers for a while, but his sales have doubled since and he has been able to keep his prices down, and so now he actually employs more workers than he did before.

Look Ahead

In some ways one has to think of automation itself depending on where you stand. Many factories today get their raw materials almost daily; they process so much so rapidly that to maintain any sizeable amount of raw stock is uneconomical, so materials have to be brought in almost daily; most companies ship daily. When you have a situation like that, the plant is no longer just by itself, it is a part of a transportation relationship. Communication between plants as a result has grown so that you now have a network of communications and flow of information. This is proceeding so fast that within the next decade problems which we are discussing here will be truly big problems that industry itself is going to have to face.

Today, manufacturing accounts for only 30% of the total of more than 80 millions gainfully employed. Manufacturing itself is large in terms of the value added in production of goods. The automated equipment provided by the engineering industries and the machinery industries that makes this possible can and does come largely in bits and pieces. And, as far as the ultimate in automation, the kind of unmanned automated process idea often discussed is beyond visibility. In most cases, the technology today doesn't make it economically feasible, but any miracle can happen tomorrow and bring to pass what at present is beyond feasibility. From an overall standpoint, it appears that the speed with which useful automation — defined as automatic production systems — the speed with which automation is going to penetrate the economy, and the hope for this in some areas, has been somewhat exaggerated.

We have been seriously interested in many of the quasi-ethical discussions raised about automation. It would seem that if automation relieves man of the physical work, there isn't much ethics involved. On the other hand, if automation relieves man of thinking something that is rational, then the question might be raised as to just what is left. However, as to the argument encountered about thinking — there's no machine invented that substitutes for the human brain. Input is critical and costly and if you put errors into the machine, then all it does is compound them faster and faster. The result is obviously useless.

Much Research Needed

Recently machines have come to aid man in making decisions. There are only systems which aid man in making decisions in situations where man alone would not be able to make decisions without such a system — some of these systems come very close to being rational systems. But there is a limitation. The process itself must be entirely formulized, sequences of action must be described as greatly at length as possible, and then you get the machine to take over. Man still has to do that much at this level. There would appear to be many functions of man with which current technology simply is unable to cope.

No Apologies Needed

In the discussion of automation it is perturbing to note an apologetic attitude among engineers. There has been a defensive attitude because of job displacement due to automation. Let us be frank about this. The purpose of automation is to displace jobs. That's what you do it for. You economize on the scarcity source — where we have production the scarcity is labor, the expense of which is unequalled. That is our most expensive input — it is the one you economize on. The purpose of automation, therefore, is to displace people, or more realistically, is to displace jobs.

Automation in agriculture is in the same category as automation in the office or in manufacturing. American agriculture provides our best illustration of automation as a completely integrated process. Some 59 years ago, for your information, there were 48% of us in this country working on farms. It took half of us out there to feed the rest. Now we have less than 5% of our working force on farms and half of these really aren't gainfully employed. We can now feed ourselves with about 3% of our working force in agriculture. This is the greatest thing that ever happened in America. We now feed ourselves with so much less manpower that it makes manpower available to have a telephone in every home — have a color TV upstairs and a black and white one in the basement. Automation in this case has resulted in a tremendous displacement of persons with some resultant social problems for sure.

When we are talking about agriculture we must recognize two different aspects — one is the actual introduction of mechanization, and the other is that the people want to live in the cities. It is uncertain as to the proportion of each in terms of effect on the movement of people. If you study the immigration of people to the cities, it is not solely an American phenomenon either. It is worldwide. This phenomenon is to some degree as a result of automation but is more so from interest in a higher standard of living.

However, we should never apologize for automation resulting in a decrease in unit employment — that's the purpose of it. Now, we have many growth industries where total employment has gone up, and pay very, very markedly up in many cases. Never apologize for this.

Of course, these transformations do effect displacement. But, there is no case could be made for the proposition that automation lowers the total requirement of manpower. The total demand is growing and there is no reason why it shouldn't continue to do so. In other words, the total demand is enhanced because greater education, training, technical skill and ability is required by this total process of technological improvement.

A Big Challenge

The area of the economy that is susceptible to the introduction of more automation in the next ten or twenty years represents a very small segment in terms of total employment in the country. We will actually be displacing workers that never existed — we are displacing jobs that never existed. The percentage in industrial employment — the blue collar — as a production force is going to continue to shrink in terms of the whole. The big area of growth is going to be in the service industries.

In conclusion, technology is undergoing continuing development for application of automation to the home, the office, the factory, the schools and the public services. The big problem and the big challenge today is to apply this developing technology.

6

Automation and Education

Grant Venn

Grant Venn, Associate Commissioner for Adult, Vocational and Library Programs, U.S. Department of Health, Education and Welfare, Office of Education, Washington, received his BSBEd., MA, ED.D, from Washington State University. Formerly a school superintendent, college professor and president, Dr. Venn's current responsibilities include manpower development and training. He has written on this subject, among others, in the light of technical change.

Automation and education may be considered from two points of view: (1) How the application of automation and technology may be used to help individuals learn more effectively; or (2) how a nation must change its educational system to prepare individuals to control and live more effectively in a technological society.

It is this second question that should primarily concern this symposium.

In this context I use the term "automation" not in a scientific sense but broadly in reference to the continuously expanding and advancing technology of the present and the near future. I will make no attempt to look into the distant future of education because I believe the next three decades will largely determine whether we can change our educational system enough to serve a technological society successfully.

Future historians will find among the characteristics of the present society in America great technological advancement, automation of repetitive work, rapid changes in the labor force, the highest unemployment rates among youth and elderly people — and the highest percentage of people engaged in education!

If these same historians could look beyond these symptoms, they would discover certain social and psychological conditions that should be improving in the world's most technically advanced nation. Instead, we find increasing fear of other people, large pockets of poor people, rising crime rates, deteriorating cities, depressed rural areas, pollution of air, water and streets, riots, racial segregation and widening opportunity gaps between the uneducated and well educated.

Gunner Myrdal, in the December 1968 issue of *Look* magazine, article "The American Conscience," tells it as it is:

"You don't get to the heart of the problem by saying the American upper and middle class are exploiting the poor people in the slums. Sometimes some do; but as a whole, the negroes are not exploited by white America. The worst thing is that with modern technology and the rise of education for the big majority, there is no demand for the labor of illiterate and semi-illiterate people. You are cutting off an under class which is not needed, not employable. This is the horrible thing, and it is true not only about the Negroes but also the poor whites, many Puerto Ricans, Mexicans, Asians and so on. It is true about all those who are really poverty-stricken."

We may argue and debate many points but it is a fact because of automation we have people who are economic liabilities today who a few years ago would have been economic assets. It is also a fact that education, as it is institutionalized in this country today, was structured, organized, financed and its purposes and objectives set when this nation was an agricultural, non-affluent, but stable society.

Conflicts from Change

These comments will be addressed primarily to the conflicts generated by an educational system, designed and conceived in a stable, agricultural, scarcity society, now functioning in a changing, technological, affluent society.

Let me hasten to add that this observation is not based on the assumption that our schools have failed, but rather, I believe, that they have been too successful in accomplishing what the society of the past asked of them.

Briefly, a hundred years ago our educational system had already been well established. It was assumed that some people would always be poor and hungry since scarcity was a condition man had always known and his social institutions had accepted. Therefore, the greatest problem society faced was how to divide among everyone an amount that would never be enough for all. The debate concerning material things dealt with the problem of how a society could divide what it has equitably.

Search for the Right Answer

In an automated society, which we know can produce if we so will it all the necessary food, shelter and clothing, the question should be asked: How do we see that everyone gets what he needs? Why not use our resources to feed the poor, house the unemployed, educate the uneducated and heal the sick?

In the past, we also assumed things changed but little, and all of man's experience tended to verify this. One of society's major concerns was: What is the right system of education, consonant with our philosophies of politics, religion and economics? There was a constant search for the right answer — for the individual who knew and the system that would always work.

In a technological society success can sometimes be a handicap, especially if it convinces an institution there is no need to change. The issue is not how does one find the one answer but rather the new problems and ways to resolve them.

Rightly or wrongly, this nation hit upon education as one of the major answers. Today, some 22,000 school districts plus more than 2,000 public and private colleges and universities form our basic educational structure. A recent Gallup poll indicated that 82 percent of this nation's adults feel that this system is doing a good to excellent job.

However, some changes have taken place since this system was created:

1. The nation's workforce can no longer absorb large numbers of uneducated people.
2. Education has become the bridge between the individual and a role in society.
3. Large segments of our people find themselves locked out of our culture because of youth, illiteracy or old age.
4. The myth that educational quality is the ability to select students "out" is no longer believed.
5. The total education gained in the "system" is inadequate for an adult role because things are changing so rapidly.
6. The educational disparity between some people and some parts of our country is so great as to cause permanent inequality.
7. It is generally recognized that all learning does not take place in the educational system.
8. Our present educational system does not serve the poor, the inner city, minority groups and those who need education most.

Therefore, we must conclude that in an automated society education is a necessity for everyone, which simply wasn't true three decades ago.

This brief and admittedly oversimplified thesis should lead us to ask some questions about education in a technological society. They cannot be answered simply but they provide the basis for discussion. They are adapted from Ernest O. Melby's "The Community School: A Social Imperative," in the October 1968 issue of *The Community School and Its Administration.*

Is our educational system obsolete? Does special help for

the disadvantaged, the slow learner, the ghetto child, the unemployed and the delinquent really blind us to a larger failure with all youth and all people?

Why does an affluent nation tolerate slums?

Why is it that educated white people fail to understand what it means to be black in America?

Why do we refuse to give equality and full citizenship to our minority groups?

Why have we so little concern for injustice and compassion for the less fortunate?

Why don't we invest more in people when in a technological society we know our human resource is our greatest wealth?

Today's Specifics

Accelerating scientific and technological advances are revolutionizing our economy and our social institutions. On the one hand, in occupations requiring extensive education and training we are experiencing demands which are far outstripping trained manpower available. On the other hand, opportunities for the untrained and partially educated to find initial placement and to learn on the job are diminishing. Education must prepare or at least play a large role in preparing people to adapt to the pressing manpower changes they must face. This role extends far beyond providing skill training for those who want it. It includes training the unprepared for work, coping with a rapidly changing society, and assuring equal opportunities for all regardless of race or color.

Change itself is certain, but it is also certain to be slow when applied to people. Computer technology can change almost overnight. But it takes time to change a farm boy into a computer programmer. It may take even more time to change his teacher. That all these changes are actually taking place, regardless, is something of a tribute to the basic adaptability of the human animal.

Changes appearing are so startling they test to the utmost the present generation's adaptive capacities, stability, and wisdom. Unlike their parents, this generation of young people does not know the meaning of stability. It is engulfed in a whirlpool of change. Therefore, for the first time we must educate young people and re-educate adults to new dimensions of time and change. Taught to rebel against change, people require powerful incentives to accept change. Schools must teach students to accept the inevitability of change. We must inspire initiative and ease adapting to and growing with technological change.

The fact that social changes are running far behind technological changes is an indictment of the social scientists and, I'm afraid, the educators. Even sadder, it is an indictment of the purposes of education as seen by the public.

It is a serious matter that during a period of maximum national economic growth and increasing gross national product, with the total unemployment rate below 4 percent, we still have 18 percent of the young people in the nation — those between the ages of 16 and 22 — unemployed.* Even more critical is the 30 percent of Negro youth unemployed in the same age group. All this while we face the greatest shortage of technical manpower ever known in this country because of the increasing impact of technology.

This dilemma also is the major challenge facing education today. It is not possible — it is not even desirable — to separate education, especially education for the world of work, from the basic problems of our society.

---

*Editors' Note: Although the Dept. of Labor Statistics accumulates data on employment starting with age 14, a practice dating back to the last century, it is well known that child labor laws prohibit to a great extent and virtually eliminate the 14-19 year group from any meaningful participation in the workforce.

I think the best perspective on this problem can be achieved by outlining some of the basic issues facing educators and society as a whole.

One of these is the fact that 30 percent of the youth in this country drop out before completing high school. Are we really going to teach everyone to read and write and then hope that somehow they acquire vocational skills? They can't without an educational level which allows continuous learning.

Also, there is no clearcut way for many adolescents in our culture to move from childhood and adolescence into a contributing role as an adult in society. The dropouts, and many other youngsters in our schools, do not see — and the schools do not provide — the skills by which they can move from adolescence to adulthood. Youngsters don't know what options are available in a technological society or the educational requirements needed to secure an entry into the workforce.

A Geographic Problem

Another issue is integration. Not only racial integration, but one which may be more serious as far as the economic achievement of people is concerned. As we change rapidly, and increasing educational levels are demanded, people tend to become segregated for economic reasons. There is geographical isolation or segregation which results from certain rural areas being left out of the mainstream of technological development and educational improvement.

We have another major issue which is somewhat buried. That is the educational level of adults already in the workforce. Over half the adults in the United States aged 25 in 1960 had not graduated from high school. These statistics from the 1960 census mean that the majority of our adults face a real problem adjusting to a technological society.

Finally, the most serious issue that we need to consider is prevention and development vs. remediation and correction. Where do we put our bets in the long run? We simply cannot forget those who are not educated; those isolated and locked out of society for whatever reason. But what do we do about the young people in our schools now? What do we do about adults needing retraining before they can get jobs? Do we simply allow them to drop out and then correct this later through remedial programs, or do we invest our money earlier to prevent human failure and develop our human resources?

Remedial Vs. Preventive Education

In recent years, much of the nation's emphasis in manpower training programs has been on remedial efforts for youth and adults who have left the school system. Experience has shown that these are far more expensive and less effective than education programs designed for serving young people which are both preventive and developmental. Thus, for maximum effectiveness, long-range manpower policy of the federal government must include building into the elementary and secondary and post-secondary schools of the country the capabilities of serving all the education needs of youth. The public schools are one of the few institutions to which virtually all of our population is exposed. Doesn't it make far more sense from the viewpoints of both efficiency and effectiveness to strengthen and to modify this system to adequately serve the needs of all our population rather than to establish and fund additional systems of education? To the extent that the nation devotes resources toward improving education for work within the existing public school framework, the need for extensive large-scale emergency programs such as those operated under MDTA or Job Corps will be reduced.

It is my position, therefore, that it is in the best interests of this nation to allocate the financial resources necessary to allow the schools to serve all of our people. The education legislation enacted over the last five years enabled us to make great strides toward achieving this goal. Vocational offerings at all levels and for all persons have been greatly expanded all over the country. New and innovative approaches for reaching the disadvantaged are underway in all states. Strengthened research, experimental and demonstration efforts hold great promise for the future. Accomplishments as a result of this legislation are already observable. There are nearly 9 million enrolled in vocational education today compared to 4.2 million in 1963. Despite this increase it is clear that our efforts must be considerably expanded.

The school is the one institution in which all of our young people come together in one way or another at one time or another. Nowhere else can we really focus our resources so effectively. That is why it is essential the schools must be changed from "selecting-out" to "including-in" institutions — for the rich and the poor, the old and the young, the bright and the slow.

The whole educational system — the curricula, the instructional programs, their relationships to each other — must take into account present and future occupational opportunities and all kinds of people. We need an exploratory occupational education program for all junior high school students. It is during the 7th, 8th and 9th grades that the majority of our young people drop out of school.

Prevocational Instruction

Many of the approximately 10 million boys and girls enrolled in junior high schools in urban centers today have little knowledge or understanding of the world of work, or of the opportunities for the many careers in various occupational fields. Even in small towns and rural communities where work is no stranger to youths, their knowledge of the occupational spectrum is limited. In too many instances the children have a narrow concept of the ways in which people earn their livelihood other than the superficial knowledge gained through observation of activities being carried on in business and industry in their immediate neighborhoods.

Since the world of work of the future will be even more complicated than now, students will need more education than ever. School dropouts will have even less chance of competing in the future than they have now. The schools must, therefore, do everything they can to keep students in school.

An occupational orientation and guidance program must be installed in our school system beginning at the junior high school level. Students must be made acquainted with the wide variety of jobs that business and industry has to offer, with the skills that will be needed for each of these occupations, and the compensations they offer.

Efforts should be directed toward providing a base for the development of an occupationally oriented program for all students in grades 10-12, and a skill development program for some in high school which will lead to further post-secondary on-the-job or in-school preparation for careers. In this way every student can be encouraged to make a tentative choice of an occupational objective and be given an opportunity and a means for achieving it. The educational program once started must be continuous, with expert counseling and guidance provided at the time each student makes a change in his goal. The program must be flexible enough to permit crossovers from one curriculum to another without penalty.

We want to give youngsters a broad understanding of occupations so that all students will have a better appreciation of the world of work and their opportunities for employment and purposeful contributions to society. The idea is not to force them to make a vocational choice but simply to give them a broad base from which they can make intelligent choices when the time comes.

It is important, therefore, that our schools and colleges make orientation to the world of work, and the exploration of broad occupational fields, an integral part of the total educational program of each individual.

This does not mean, however, that the arts and humanities should be de-emphasized. Automation is making it possible for employees to work shorter hours and have more leisure time. The better background in the arts and humanities that students obtain the more they will enjoy and make fruitful use of their leisure time.

At the same time we must help each student develop thoroughly through educational part-time work experience. It would promote in him a sense of achievement in school-related work experience, enlarge his educational opportunities, recognize the value of work, and establish better communications between educators and employers or customers. These experiences should primarily teach young people employability skills.

Cooperative Education — Work-Study Program

The changed nature of work has virtually barred many of our young people from a realistic role in the work world. In effect, they have no opportunity to contribute. However, every individual should be able to recognize worth and dignity in himself. Education has little meaning or reality for thousands of young people who have no such present conviction and who cannot defer to a future role in society because they lack aspiration, background, environment, or proper ties with their family, their community, or their country. Programs must be developed which give every person the opportunity to serve a useful purpose.

Segments of our society are being locked out of work because of technological changes. Youths experience great difficulty in breaking into the world of work. This is not due to lack of jobs but to lack of skills. Modern technology is becoming too complicated to afford many untrained youngsters a job after graduation. Without experience they can't get jobs. And without jobs they can't get experience.

We can break this vicious cycle and give youngsters that minimum training and experience which will enable them to land that first job by giving them on-the-job training while they are in school.

Vocational Education Important

Since classroom instruction is no longer enough in today's technological world, we must help students become employable by encouraging them to combine school with a job. Schools, with the cooperation of business and industry, must offer work experience programs to students in which they can develop skills and receive credit. This program would be for all youngsters in high school who wish to take advantage of the opportunity, and it would assist needy students to continue their education. The program would be a recognized part of the total school program through grading and credit for community service work, work experience, cooperative education, and on-the-job training.

The work-experience program includes both cooperative education and work-study. Limited work-study and cooperative education programs have been in operation at the secondary level for many years in distribution and marketing, in some of the trades, and in a few other fields. The cooperative programs have been particularly successful in distributive education.

In cooperative education the student learns about an occupation in school, and he practices what he has learned on the job under the supervision of the school. The work-study program, while similar, is primarily for the purpose of providing financial assistance to needy students who otherwise would not be able to continue their vocational education. Their work time need not necessarily be spent on jobs related to their instruction. However, both cooperative education and work-study will develop employability skills and good work habits in the students.

Work experience opportunities need to be extended to as many students as possible and not restricted to a few vocational fields. These programs should be planned and operated by local school officials with responsibility for developing contacts with local industry and business and for planning arrangements which place high school age youngsters in jobs pertinent to their studies and their interests — and hopefully pertinent to what they will do when they leave high school. Introducing youngsters to the world of work has an educational as well as an economic value.

For work study or work experience programs to be successful, fulltime counseling and liaison personnel are needed in the schools. Such personnel are necessary to assure that both students and faculty participating in the programs do so as part of their education experience rather than something isolated and insulated from it. Counseling and placement arrangements which simply connect youngsters with business without regard to the dovetailing of work and education efforts will not fully satisfy this objective. Work experience programs should be seen as more than simply opportunities for school age youngsters to earn money. What the youngsters do is more important than the income they receive, and the whole enterprise needs to be viewed as an education endeavor controlled by the education officials of the local community with federal assistance.

Business and industry must provide more and better opportunities for part-time employment of students who are learning occupations. The work experience program is a primary channel for involving businessmen, industrialists and labor unions in education. They can play a vital role by informing schools of their particular requirements, supplying instructional material, machines, and part-time instructors, and by cooperating with the schools in accepting students for part-time work and supervising them in work experience programs. This cooperation will be mutually beneficial, helping the employer as well as the student.

Relevancy is Needed

An expanded work-experience program also will establish better communication between educators and other important segments of the community. It will give the student the opportunity of playing a role in the working community and will increase the holding power of the school. Students tend to drop out because they find school irrelevant and unrelated to what they are going to do for most of their lives. Work experience will provide a greater opportunity for academic and vocational experiences, will involve the students more in what they are learning and make school more relevant, thus decreasing the dropout rate. Students who do drop out will have at least some job experience to fall back on. Probably no other learning procedure can rival cooperative work experience as a motivating factor for a student to achieve the goals he has set for himself.

Just as the shops and classrooms are the laboratories for teaching and testing occupational skills, so the work experience programs are the laboratories for teaching and testing employability skills. This is the area in which our schools have failed their students more than in any other. About 95

percent of the young people who lose their first jobs lose
them not because of any lack of ability or proficiency — but
because they don't know how to get along on the job.

Work experience will enable the student to test his employability and job skills, and to evaluate his growth. Work
experience will help promote a sense of achievement in the
student, especially the one not academically inclined. It will
help the youngster recognize the value of work. He will learn
that regular attendance at school and work pays off. He will
realize that good citizenship practices and good attitudes
toward work and school are amply rewarded.

We have the responsibility — and we have the know-how —
to convert an unemployable adolescent into a productive
adult; a liability into an asset. Work experience is one of the
chief channels to accomplish this.

We also must develop new curricula in vocational education to serve youngsters now being ignored. Example: A
senior intended to go to college all through high school. But,
now he is not going to college. Maybe we need to set up for
these young people short courses of one semester or six
weeks to give them specific saleable skills. This could make
them employable with entry skills that would immediately
be profitable to an employer.

The responsibility of the schools for its students cannot be
over-emphasized. The responsibility is not just for instruction. It applies to those who leave as well as to those who
remain — to the dropouts as well as the stay-ins. It applies
both to admissions and to placement.

I am convinced that America wants its schools to look for
ways to help every individual learn and become an active
participant in society. It does not want them to be part of a
system for excluding all those who, for some reason, are not
learning well at the moment. If our education system is to
fulfill the responsibilities described, we must have greater

integration rather than separation of vocational and general education and much closer ties between educators and other groups, including employers, unions, State and local agencies such as the Employment Service, and local-community organizations. Federal policy, including that of the Department of Health, Education, and Welfare and its Office of Education, needs to seek whatever changes are necessary to integrate vocational education concerns into the public school system at all levels — primary, secondary and post-secondary.

Today the average person will need to change his occupation four or five times during his life. Dept. of Labor statistics reveal that in a single year, as many as 8 million workmen make 11.5 million job changes. Obviously, some of these result from automation and technological change. Because occupations are expected to change rapidly and because workers are expected to change jobs even more frequently, the school must no longer train for narrow specialization or simple, specific job skills, but the school must offer the student a broad basis for a variety of possible occupations. A person must be trained for clusters of jobs so that he may switch from one job to another when he chooses. Vocational educators must use new methods to train workers in the basic skills they will need to move into growing new areas.

Education for specific vocational competence should provide for built-in versatility and flexibility so that students may acquire understanding, knowledge, and skills that are transferable in a complex and changing technology. We must continue to prepare persons for entry skills, but we must now also prepare them for all aspects of a particular occupation so that they can shift from one aspect of their job to another when desirable. We must now place greater emphasis on developing "conceptual" skills rather than on the "perceptual" kinds.

Training For New Jobs

The school has a significant role and responsibility in manpower development. But the educational problems are growing as technology continues to advance. Present educational personnel must be re-educated to meet the needs of economic and social changes already well under way.

We need to gear our vocational-technical programs more realistically and more flexibly to current and anticipated employment opportunities. Several millions are unemployed today, but thousands of jobs are unfilled. Persistent unemployment and underemployment of the disadvantaged is incongruous in the face of our urgent need for trained personnel to provide more and better education, health, welfare, and other services and to cope with our increasingly sophisticated technology.

In the early application of industrial technology in our society the need was for a comparatively few people vocationally prepared as managers, engineers and administrators — and for a great mass of workers to provide the muscle power and the low-level operative skills. This workforce took the shape of a very flat triangle. Necessary skills were provided by the educational system and this was the picture until about the mid 1940's. Today manpower requirements of an increasing technological society are in the shape of a tall vase, which tapers below the top to indicate the need for administrators, researchers, planners, scientists, engineers, sales personnel, independent businessmen, technicians, programmers, teachers and the many others who use mainly cognitive skills. The vase draws in sharply at the bottom to show the decreasing demand for those who can qualify only for muscular and repetitive tasks that daily are being replaced by machines.

Increased automation will bring about an increase in the

demand for skilled labor, for technicians and professional people, and for managers. "As operations become more and more automated, personnel requirements generally move up the scale toward the management level," Roger Bolz states in his book *Understanding Automation.* "On-the-line production skills of machine-line varieties will gradually diminish and higher levels will grow. While this trend is taking place, a good percentage of the jobs will be translated to new areas developing." *(Understanding Automation,* pp. 174-175.) Vocational educators must constantly be alert about these developing skill demands, and they must adjust their curriculums accordingly.

As plant operations become more sophisticated, training and study for greater technical competence, increased supervisory skill, and more teamwork are needed. The growing area of independent small business creates an even greater need for such competencies.

Transition from School to Work

The world of work is becoming more complex. More kinds of skills and knowledge are needed today, and a greater variety is expected to be needed in the future. The concomitant opportunities available in the workaday world also are growing. If our students are to take advantage of these opportunities and if they are to fill the openings which must be filled, they must have available more and better vocational counseling to make them aware of these opportunities and to guide them to the skill areas in which they could perform best.

The school now assumes responsibility for the college-bound student — to get that student into the college program that will fit him best. Public schools at the secondary level have never accepted the responsibility for placement of their students in entry-level jobs in the same wholehearted way they have assisted other students who continue their education to get into college and universities but, if more than 80 percent of our young people between high school and the baccalaureate degree must enter the workforce directly, it seems to me that our schools must also assume the responsibility for entry job placement guidance. If they do so they will become the best place for every young person to get help for that first job.

Teachers are better acquainted with the interests, abilities, and characteristics of students than anyone else. Therefore, schools should be in the best position to guide the student into the kind of job that suits him best, in which he will be happiest, and in which he will be most productive. Secondary and post-secondary schools should take on the responsibility for the transition from school to work for all students who are not going on to college. This responsibility must extend to early school dropouts, to high school graduates, to graduates of technical institutes and community colleges, as well as to college graduates. Schools should be in direct and continuous contact with employers, and labor unions. Initial placement should be an integral part of school responsibility. Business, industry and labor unions can help make the transition for the youngsters smoother and more effective. In fact, the success of a placement program will require the deep involvement of business, industry and labor. Through this cooperation, business and industry will obtain high calibre employees — better educated and better trained.

In providing this new service, schools should cooperate with the local State Employment Service. The placement activity should be carried out cooperatively with the State Employment Agencies, utilizing Employment Services personnel where possible and integrating them into the counseling and teaching structure of the school. A close working relationship between the Employment Security Service and the school system at the State and local levels can provide placement and follow-up service for all students.

If our public education system is to continue to be the chief source for preparing youths for the world of work, it must assume the responsibility for helping them make the transition from school to work.

Continuous Education

A fundamental change that has taken place in our culture is the acceleration of the rate of accumulation of knowledge. This phenomenon is accompanied by the generally accepted view that there is no place in the modern world for the uneducated and the untrained, and that there is only a slight difference between the uneducated and undereducated, or the untrained and the undertrained. But in too many instances our schools continue practices which were once valid but are increasingly inadequate; namely, that the schools can prepare an individual in four years, or eight years, for a lifetime career.

Fewer jobs will hold up for the entire working life of a person in the future. Roger Bolz states that, "No matter how attached the workman may be to any particular job, it is imperative that he recognize there is no static condition in the world of business. The only constant is change." (*Understanding Automation,* page 54.)

Many industrial corporations recognize this fact and are offering their employees opportunity for further education both in the plant and with outside schools and institutes. In this way employees gain new information and new skills and are able to step into new jobs when automation eliminates or changes the old jobs. It also is advantageous to management because through such continuous education programs firms are able to retain proven and dependable employees despite the fast changes of an automated economy.

Mr. Bolz states further that, "In the transition ahead youth will face the need for developing a new philosophy of life, a new philosophy of work, and a new philosophy of service. Gradually emphasis in work will change in the direction of mental effort. Old ideas of labor will disappear. The coming age will require youth on a large scale to continue studying and become educated far beyond that now known. Universally, education must become a lifelong process."

The strength of our society depends upon the full development of every individual, and thus we must gear our educational system to the concept of continuing education in its broadest sense. To utilize effectively the phenomenon of the explosion of knowledge, an individual must become oriented to the world of work at an early age through practice and acquire the ability to adapt relevant knowledge — an ability he will need throughout his working career.

All high schools must, of course, provide opportunities for the development of vocational competence as well as preparation for post-high school education. However, even more basic than the academic and vocational characteristics of the educational program is the development in each student of the ability and motivation for self-learning and continuing education.

To accomplish this task, our educational institutions must operate the year round to a much greater extent than they have up to now.

Adult education must assume a much greater role in updating skills and promoting continued learning about one's work. The notion of refresher or extension courses, so well accepted in many professions, must become accepted as a routine course of action for people in industry and government and must be applied to workers at all echelons. Further, there is a great need for better facilities for counseling, guidance, and placement at the adult level.

According to Mr. Bolz, all industries and businesses should

"have a continuing education and training program in force whether formal or informal. To match the needs of increasing automation, training and education are needed for all personnel from management to hourly workers. Expanded horizons offered by such programs relate directly to improvements in the efficiency and variety of talents brought to bear on competitive everyday operations." *(Understanding Automation,* page 73.)

If the work week is cut as a result of automation, that cut should not result solely in released time, but a large part of the time should be used for education and training.

Instead of graduation from school being thought of as the completion of education, we know today that it should be only the beginning of learning for nearly everyone. It is imperative that we have available for all, on a continuing basis, educational experiences that will make it possible for all to cope with the changing technology and the changing jobs in our economy.

Education for Greater Leisure

The trend is toward less time spent on the job; more leisure time. Although the occupational week has remained static in recent years, there is indication that the work week will be shorter in the future. The length of the occupational week alone is not sufficient indication of the trend toward less time on the job. The work week is based on the number of hours for which an employee is paid. But employees are being paid for more and more hours during which they do not work. They have longer vacations and more liberal sick leave. Statistics now measure only hours paid; if they measured hours at work, a greater trend toward leisure time would be evident.

There also is an increasing trend toward early retirement. Some people retire because they are not qualified to hold new jobs. Projections by the Bureau of Labor Statistics show that for 1975 and 1980 less than 25 percent of men older than 65 will remain in the labor force.

People frequently find it difficult to find a satisfying role in life as familiar responsibilities are sloughed off. Increasingly, in older life there is a greater demand for meaning. This is never wholly satisfied by educational programs which stress do-it-yourself activities or some of the leisure-time arts. However, learning, or at least learning not associated with do-it-yourself activities, has little place in the thinking of the majority of the people with leisure today. People must, therefore, be educated to enjoy their increasing leisure time, as they are now trained for productive work. They must be educated to use their leisure fruitfully. It is the job of education to make this leisure time a profit to the retiree and his associates rather than a frustration. We must help people find a meaning in life outside their jobs.

People want to feel that they are progressing as human beings. If it is a fundamental need of every man to feel that he is eternally going forward, adult learning certainly has a place in the proper planning of man's life. It can give a direction to man's maturing and aging through all his years.

Self-improvement, with a goal of community or national service, should be made to appear more attractive than ever-expanding play time. This is especially important today when the complications of an increasingly highly technical existence call for more group attention upon the problems of community, national, and international existence.

With more leisure in the future, it will be up to educators to give persons with leisure a strong constructive orientation toward more satisfying and beneficial use of their time.

Conclusions

There is conclusive evidence that automation and technological advance have a profound impact on our society and have resulted in a myriad of problems that must be solved if this nation is to continue to grow and prosper.

Many of these problems can be solved through education. However, to do so, our educational system must change its direction, its role in society and must assume new and greater responsibilities.

That this is necessary can be ascertained by facing these facts:

1. U.S. Employment Service studies show a 25 percent increase in new job titles since the last study.
2. Every person will change jobs three to five times in his lifetime.
3. Despite our unemployment rate being less than four percent, for youths between 16 and 22 years of age it is 18 percent and for Negroes in that age group it is double that.
4. Nearly one million boys and girls drop out of our public schools before graduating from high school each year.
5. There is no lack of jobs in the nation but lack of skills. Modern technology is becoming too complicated to afford many untrained youngsters a job before or after graduation.
6. More than 90 percent of young people who lose their first job lose it, not because of any lack of ability, but because they don't know how to get along on the job.
7. Productive human resources are a nation's greatest asset.

Educators have been forced to reach the conclusion that our present educational system has proved to be less than successful with the poor, with the inner city, with the black people and other minority groups. In many respects our educational system is obsolete and, to solve the problems of this technological age, must change drastically. It must assume responsibility for not only the academic-minded boy and girl who wants to go to college, but for the nonlearner, the underachiever, the youth who finds little in school to interest him or relevancy between the classroom and his future, the physically and mentally handicapped, and the dropout.

This admittedly is a large order but it can be filled. However, to fill it our schools must:

1. Become "including - in," rather than "selecting - out" institutions.

2. Give courses in occupational orientation to seventh, eighth and ninth graders so they may learn about the world of work, see some relevancy between what they are studying and what they will be doing as adults, and stimulate their interest by widening their horizons and options.

3. Give every high school student some vocational education and work experience so that he may have at least one job entry skill and learn how to get along on a job.

4. Be responsible for getting graduates and dropouts jobs which they are capable of doing, in which they have interest, and in which they can advance. This should also hold true for the physically and mentally handicapped students.

5. Become involved with the community through work experience programs by seeking the advice and cooperation of business, industry and labor unions in the community; in this way develop truly community oriented schools that serve the needs of the community and its youth.

6. Teach our affluent and middle-class students what it means to be on "the outside looking in" in America, why we have slums, the meaning of equality and citizenship for everyone, the meaning of justice, tolerance and compassion.

If our educators and our schools are dedicated to these propositions the future of this nation is assured and the American Dream will become a reality for virtually all of our boys and girls.

BIBLIOGRAPHY

1. Bolz, Roger W., *Understanding Automation: Elements for Managers*. Cleveland, Ohio, Penton Publishing Co., 1966. 181 p.

2. *Education and Training, Learning for Jobs*, 1968; Report of the Secretary of Health, Education, and Welfare to the Congress on Manpower Development and Training. (FS 5.287: 97020-68) $ .60.

3. Levitan, Sar A., and Garth L. Mangum, *Making Sense of Federal Manpower Policy* (Policy Papers in Human Resources and Industrial Relations No. 2), Ann Arbor, Mich., The Institute of Labor and Industrial Relations, March 1967.

4. Levitan, Sar A., *Vocational education and Federal policy*. Kalamazoo, Michigan, W.E. Upjohn Institute for Employment Research, 1963. 22 p.

5. Mangum, Garth L., "The Development of Manpower Policy, 1961-65," *Dimensions of Manpower Policy: Programs and Research*, Baltimore, The Johns Hopkins Press, 1966.

6. Melby, Ernest O., "The Community School: A Social Imperative," *The Community School and Its Administration*, vol. 7, No. 2, p. 1 - 4. October 1968.

7. Myrdal, Gunner, "In Stockholm, Gunner Mydral talks about: the American Conscience with J. Robert Moskin," *Look*, vol. 32, No. 26, p. 32-36. December 24, 1968.

8. *Notes and Working Papers Concerning the Administration of Programs Authorized Under Vocational Education Act of 1963, Public Law 88-210, As Amended*, Prepared for the Subcommittee on Education of the Committee on Labor and Public Welfare, United States Senate, March 1968. (Availabel from the Committee)

9. Theobald, Robert, *The Challenge of Abundance*. N.Y. C.N. Potter, 1961.

10. Theobald, Robert, *The Free Men and Free Markets*. M.Y. C.N. Potter, 1963.

11. U.S. Department of Labor, *Manpower Report of the President* Washington, U.S. Government Printing Office, 1965.

12. U.S. Department of Health, Education, and Welfare, *Education and Training: Expanding the Choices*. Washingtion, U.S. Government Printing Office, 1967.

7

Education Must Relate to a Way of Life

Chairman:
Ralph W. Tyler

Deliberations on the Educational Aspects of Automation

Ralph W. Tyler, Director Emeritus, Center for Advance Study in the Behavioral Sciences, Science Research Associates, holds an AB, Doane College; AM, University of Nebraska; Ph.D, University of Chicago. Dr. Tyler is chairman of the National Commissions on Resources for Youth and on Cooperative Education. He is senior advisor, Science Research Associates, a subsidiary of IBM.

A large segment of the general public has historically viewed education as a selecting out process — those who survived the course were rewarded with wealth and the benefits of non-material cultural values. The system had established credibility. It was a channel to affluence and the good life. The general public still perceives education as doing a basically good job but questions are being asked. With the new technology, the new society, what kind of role or function must the school play? What should it be asked to do and expected to do?

What wasn't necessary, or profitable, to do a few decades ago may now be imperative. The question must be resolved as to the responsibilities of schools in the total education process. Will the technical school serve the needs of an automated society adequately if the conventional educational role schools once provided for technical training is allowed to vanish. Also, there are things that people do not learn in schools! If this training is not provided now outside the school, what must be the school's response?

One of the present aims of the schools is teaching the so-called disadvantaged. Fifty years ago children dropped out of school all along the line to go to work. This unskilled labor was available and didn't require schooling. Today, there is little call for such labor. Very few jobs are available today which do not require some degree of literacy.

Learning Image Needed

There is a serious lack in the educational system, contrasting it, for example, with what happens in industry where there are motivational and incentive guidelines for profitability and efficiency of operation for expansion of the enterprise. The changing character of the labor force places much greater emphasis upon intellectual skills and social skills and less upon physical strength and manual dexterity. One consequence has been new opportunities for women in the labor force. In the decade of the 50's, half the new jobs were taken by women! Part of the problem, then, from the point of view of boys from working class families is that their image of the male occupation involves physical strength and manual dexterity which being taken over by machines. Their image of female work is intellectual and social.

For children of middle-class families this is not a handicap. They see their fathers in intellectual occupations, sales or areas using social skills. So again we have the problem of shifting from one generation to another. How much do we really know about the nature of the shift — the value of skills, the attitudes and behaviors that produce a skill?

We are now for the first time at the point in the history of man where every man must have the basic skills of learning. This means communication skills, verbal skills and the capability to enable every man to continue learning and relearning throughout life. This is a different kind of thing than in the past. The school establishment is at least giving lip service to the concept. Learning "how to learn" has become an important objective in education.

In material production we lean heavily upon individual choices and the free market. We are now able to produce and distribute goods so that at last estimate in 1967 we used only 40 per cent of our labor force to produce and distribute material goods and 60 per cent for nonmaterial things as education, health services, recreation, social services, engineering and science, accounting and management. If this kind of change takes place, isn't it reasonable to expect that the nature of human individual choice will largely determine the direction in which enterprises will move? If so, we must ask what people will want from an affluent society — now they can afford to pay for other than material goods. Right now, it seems, the desire is for more health service, more education services, more recreation. If this trend continues what sorts of people will be required to provide these services and what kind of education should they get?

Analyses being made for the educational establishment at both secondary and college levels put the final emphasis on development of intellectual and social skills. How can the schools and colleges do more than they have been doing to get more people into these categories?

One response of the people in education is to give more and more consideration to cooperative education — coordinating the work between schools and industry to facilitate the entry of people into the work force. Another is to hold the place of the drop-out in case he wishes to return and to facilitate his re-entry into the school. Also considered is the notion of pacing and spacing in the educational program to better serve individual needs and interests.

We have a tendency in our society to place the lowest social value on the things that are most essential. For example, a food service worker has little social status — yet we all have to eat. A little imagination can work wonders here! One company sent one of its food service workers to a culinary institute in New York for a summer training program. He came back a completely revitalized person. He wears his chef's hat at a little more rakish angle than before. This nation has not dealt with the fact that many skills which are vitally needed in our society are not looked upon as worthy of consideration and we turn our backs on the whole problem. Automation in the kitchen and the automation of the pre-preparation of food may be one solution, but automation in the serving of food may never be.

Why should education in our society be restricted to a single area on the occupational spectrum? If automation does indeed mean more free time, why can't individuals develop additional skills? Perhaps the "intellectual" can do manual work as well if he finds it enjoyable. A dual role may be the answer with part of each year devoted to activity having for a purpose a social benefit.

Because the total hours required for manufacturing are decreasing there is a current fallacy that total working force hours are also decreasing. But, as people move into nursing and teaching and so on, the work hours do not decrease. Studies show that in typical communities the number of hours worked per week by the total labor force hasn't changed in 20 years. Although working hours may be lessening in some manufacturing industries, the shift to services has offset this trend in the society at large. And, in areas where the work week does decrease, there is a point at which "moonlighting" fills the gap.

Education to Professionalize

Nevertheless, increased automation will bring about increased leisure in some fashion. Increased leisure must necessarily have educational implications. This involves adult education. Ironically, the majority of the states in the country right now, through statutes or constitutional provisions, prohibit the expenditure of funds for the education of persons over 21 years of age. In these states, adult programs must be self supporting. Those persons who need the education most have an economic barrier which is difficult to overcome.

Perhaps education can be applied to "professionalize" low-status occupations in the production and service industries. In agriculture, for example, we have an industry that has had an enormous productivity increase through the mechanization and rationalization of its procedures, with a tremendous reduction in the labor force. Yet that labor force which remains as hired workers is poorly trained and has the problem of low status. Still, the hired farm worker remains one of the vital occupations — one for whose services there is great demand. It is possible to train these people, to professionalize this occupation so that it becomes more attractive to the worker and more dependable to the employer. Some of the stigmas associated with these occupations are governmentally imposed — for example, they do not qualify for collective bargaining, do not qualify for workman's compensation, were not protected by minimum wages until recently.

Perhaps we are talking about a new type of farm worker. The facilities to train this man and the public willingness to train him is often not there. There are many cultural barriers to this type of training, race relations being one of the major impediments. There is the fear that large-scale training for farm workers will lead them to demand more pay and lead them off the farm into other occupations.

Two kinds of questions are raised. One has to do with what technology generates or demands from education for people who have to work with it. The other question is associated with occupational shifts resulting from technology and the education required for these shifts in occupational roles.

We have millions of persons in this society who lack education and the gap between these people and their ability to become involved and participate in the on-going work of society as functioning individuals is becoming greater and greater. It appears that more and more money will have to be spent for remedial and corrective measures at a very severe level of difficulty. The society has not yet been willing to invest enough money in terms of a transitional kind of preventive program. We must fit together the educational facilities and programs with the consumer of the educational product — business and industry — in a cooperative arrangement to begin to get to some of these problems. This may be the pattern a decade from now.

In the meantime many of our young people cannot see the school program as relevant to what they want. The schools really are not seen as viable vehicles by which these people can become effective individuals. Why can't we build into our schools more variety right now? This is necessary to provide the required options.

One recent study indicated that the children of college-educated parents knew less about the occupational options open to them than did the children of parents who had not been to college. The general objective of the children of the college-educated is to get to college. But in terms of career concepts and the adult role, they are narrow and uninformed. If you come home from work with a briefcase, it may be difficult to explain to a child what work that involves.

All of these events will have an impact on the school. Pressures are evolving from many groups to change the patterns in our schools. We still have the normal curve. Those institutions listed as great educational institutions are those which have the highest degree of selectivity in those students they admit. Quality is often interpreted more in the selectivity of the institution rather than how well it meets whatever its objectives may be. Educators tend to be sensitive about the educational achievements of particular systems, yet these data will be necessary if we are to assess systematically the effectiveness of educational enterprise. Today, we need more information on the kinds of schools we have.

Perhaps schools should be responsible for dropout rate as a qualification for accreditation. Again, perhaps schools should be responsible for the student entering the workforce in the same way they feel responsible for getting a student into college.

Doing different things in the schools will create new methodologies. There will be various kinds of teaching games, programmed instruction, using more closely paced methods of conditioned learning. Business and industry can lend significant support to the development of these methodologies. Schools may be expected to contract directly with industry for their development. The companies through their organizational ability have learned to do things effectively where the education system does not have the ability to move in quickly.

Growth in Services?

Although automation may be increasing productivity in the manufacturing area, this is not the case with services. Some services are beginning to cost more than the consumer will pay and some skilled trades in the service sector have become virtually unknown in small towns. If you want something serviced these days you may find that you will have to do it yourself. Anyone concerned with training people for the service sector must face up to the fact that there may be areas where services are rapidly disappearing. In addition, there are others that technology has eliminated or have priced themselves out of existence. How will the education apparatus we are seeking to design face up to this?

There is an increase in the number of paraprofessionals in many areas, but in nursing there is a tremendous shortage of paraprofessionals. Certain of these services have been priced out of the market — so society is training paraprofessionals who do not stay — for them, these are temporary jobs. So society is confronted with the never ending task of trying to recruit and train paraprofessionals. It is doubtful whether these are entry jobs into professional careers.

One solution, then, to the problem of low-level occupations is to make them entry positions in a career development pattern. If we can achieve the flexibility to make these positions entry points in an upward career pattern in lieu of the four years of college we can create another option pattern. Some persons will be attracted to these paraprofessional positions because they do offer mobility yet nevertheless remain as they fulfill their levels of aspiration and skill.

There are currently reputed to be somewhere between three and four million jobs unfilled owing to lack of skills ranging from the executive to tool and die making. More and more young people appear to have the desire to move into two-year and four-year college programs which do not meet the needs of society, even though these needs are projected 20 years in advance. How do we plan to fill these important positions which even automation will not eliminate? What kinds of changes can we introduce into our schools to cope with these needs? Before much can be done there are certain institutional arrangements and legal restraints which must be faced.

We are going to have to do something about the compulsory education laws; we are going to have to do something about the minimum wage laws; we are going to have to do something about the child labor laws! Our educational units — towns and counties — are archaic. We are just now by accident developing into social, cultural, economic educational units that need to be defined in a different way. New York . City has more in common with Bergen County, New Jersey, and Bucks County, Pennsylvania than it does with Buffalo, New York.

There are also ticklish questions of federal-state relationships. The state must share in problems with the federal government. There is the issue of the allocation of financial support for the schools and the issue of the allocation of controls. As a percentage of gross national product, we are spending no more on education today than we did during the depression. We now spend about 51 billion for education — about 35 billions for the public schools and about 15 billions for higher education. The federal contribution for public schools is a little over eight per cent.

Change and the New

Automation as change sets new patterns and creates problems. But lack of change would also create problems. Today, industry tends to bear the blame for problems attributed to automation. Industry therefore needs to recognize the problems, real or mythical, which are attributed to this technology. Industry must define these problems and make the effort to help solve them. Business is already playing an important role and this Symposium on Automation and Society sponsored by the University of Georgia with Reliance Electric Company is only one manifestation of this effort on the part of industry.

There are many problems associated with the process of change which automation did not cause. Other changes created the need for automation. Every time it is decided to raise the status of a person without the individual contributing productivity increase equivalent to the amount his compensation has increased, automation is invited. In industry as wages were increased, those tasks which were not economically viable were automated. Automation was the result rather than the cause. Automation is also a response to scarcity of labor and facilitates an expanding economy which would otherwise be seriously constrained by deficiencies, quantitative or qualitative, in the labor force. The important concern is not to place blame but to consolidate forces and come to grips with the problems of a rapidly changing technology of which automation is a significant segment. The important thing is to recognize the existence of the problem and try to do something about it.

Change Calls for Union Participation

In assisting people in adjusting to a highly technological society, education may be the answer. In the past, labor unions had a big role in education with the apprenticeship system, for developing many needed skills — bricklaying, the carpentering, and so on. Today this is largely missing. Unions are functioning like 19th century craft guilds, and are very much dominated by depression psychology with limited jobs. The challenge to unions is to participate in the educational process in terms of the needs of the times and in the catalytic process of job placement.

In the 30's there was a cleavage between the craft unions and industrial unions. There is still reluctance on the part of an industrial union to perpetuate a craft system. Industrial unions resist specialized craft training to maintain equality among their workers and avoid separate groups. Reverberations about this are rife among skilled workers in industrial unions — people who have gone through three or four-year apprenticeship programs. Apprentice-trained workers as a part of the total labor force have been declining percentagewise for some time.

If not apprenticeship, then what training is needed to prepare workers for entry into the labor force? Industry frequently does not want men without experience, and without a job the worker cannot get the experience: the problem then is how to provide the experience. Vocational training programs are one answer. Some unions have recognized this need and have supported vocational training programs. How much responsibility for training should rest with the union?

Mobility is another aspect of the training problem from the point of view of the individual employer. Industries can invest large amounts in training only to lose the services of these employees to other firms. It takes about $50,000 to train a computer programmer: his pay for two and one half years, computer time, training time for instructors, supervision and so on. The average computer programmer and analyst has changed jobs several times before he is 30 years of age. This is one of the very serious problems with training in industry. Society has not lost his services but the particular industry which provided his training has.

From the point of view of economic development, a rigid labor force would be undesirable. This is an international problem; the responsibility does not stop here. Training in industry by industry may be the best form of vocational training. The training of people internationally is not new to American society; many of our technical people came from the countries of Europe during the last century or so.

Training in an industrial setting tends to be very effective because of that setting. Students punch time clocks, work in shifts, and are exposed to many instructors rather than one. Some of the poorest performers in school do well training in an industrial environment. But, lack of job opportunities in rural communities force these people to migrate. How do we provide rural youngsters opportunities for developing skills required for employment elsewhere?

One major problem is the lack of training of teachers themselves in the new technologies and their implications. We are just now turning out our first generation of teachers with some automation background. Teachers appear reluctant to be retrained themselves — they are not going to the trouble, the effort, the time to learn. Our educational system lacks long-range planning. We need to identify the occupations that are needed in the next five to ten years. We need to plan the education system to provide not only the facilities but also the teachers. This is an investment problem and it is an input-output problem. We have no good planning process involving education, industry and government. Today schools are training for some unknown set of requirements!

In the past industry itself was operating essentially as an educational system. Work was simple enough and nontechnical enough that one could get a job and work on up to get an education. With the virtual closing of that broad-based system there is need to substitute another route for entry. The person who phases out of education phases into the market place at some level, even it if is the welfare market. The trauma of the transition now faces people of all ages when old occupations phase out. The high school or college graduate faces a transition, often years of schooling, into the marketplace where a different set of values are found. The transition may be easier for the dropout than for the graduate.

How can the nation change its educational system to prepare individuals to live more effectively in a technological environment? Does this mean the system should train him for a job? To what extent are we concerned with how individuals can live as individuals and as people? Shall we educate the whole man? Shall we plan to educate people for the leisure we are told automation will bring?

In the next few decades the pressure on the educational establishment is going to come from American industry. Up to now the establishment has been pretty much an inner-directed entity. It has also been a closely-knit political system. The educational establishment is now becoming other-directed, and who the other is becomes very important.

There will be many bids to take over. There are the dynamics of new pressure groups, including business and industry. Industrialists, scientists and other technologically-oriented persons are becoming active in the educational establishment.

Summary

Automation has an impact on education in two ways: it has developed technologies and devices that aid the learning process, and it has been a powerful factor in setting new tasks for our schools and colleges. The major time in these discussions was devoted to the latter subject.

Automation and the applications of science and technology to agriculture, industry, national defense and the health services have sharply shifted the composition of the U.S. labor force. Last year only five per cent of those employed were in unskilled occupations, while increasing demand was in technical, managerial and service occupations in the health services, education services, recreation service, social services and science, engineering, accounting and administration. Thus, few people are able to find good paying jobs who have little or no education or training while the strongest demand is for people with more than high school education. When this situation is compared with past history, great educational changes are clearly necessary. Heretofore, about 20 per cent of our children had not attained the level of education required for employment above the unskilled level, 40 per cent had not attained the equivalent of high school graduation, and less that 15 per cent had reached the level of college graduation. The new requirements of our complex technological society thus set three new tasks for our educational institutions:

1. To enable all, or almost all, children to gain a functional elementary education.

2. To enable three-fourths of our youth to gain a functional high school education.

3. To enable at least one-half of our youth to gain effective post-high school education.

Obstacles will have to be overcome in order to accomplish these tasks. A much more flexible educational system will be required to suit the needs of students having a vast difference in backgrounds. This means sharp changes in curricula and in learning and teaching activities, beginning in the early childhood years. Similar problems are faced as new groups enter high schools and colleges.

To solve the difficulty of effecting changes within well-established institutions like our schools and colleges, it is proposed to develop competing educational institutions to stimulate new and improved practices. Cooperation between industry and education could make more flexible the transitions and entry points from school to work. Also, the important potential of cooperative education, the planned alternation of work and study, could be more widely adopted. More imaginative use of new technologies to aid student learning is also seen as a means for meeting the new educational tasks. Systematic efforts are needed to develop "student-tutoring-student" arrangements for enhancing the effectiveness and efficiency of education.

In general, these discussions took an optimistic view of the possibility of accomplishing the new educational tasks. A thorough-going review of American education in terms of a systems analysis of learning and teaching should reveal promising ways of stimulating, guiding and facilitating learning that, although new to schools and colleges, offer promise of marked improvement in our national efforts in education.

8

Impact of Automation on Organization of Society

Frederick L. Bates

Frederick L. Bates, Chairman of the Department of Sociology and Anthropology, University of Georgia, earned a BA, MA, Sociology, The George Washington University; Ph.D, Sociology, The University of North Carolina. Dr. Bates' principal interests lie in social structure and social change, themes that are related in a number of his books and articles; the most recent, a monograph entitled *The Structure of Occupations*.

Automation as an engineering phenomenon may be discussed more or less objectively. When, however, we enter into a discussion of the impact of automation on society, vested interests, personal values, beliefs and uninformed opinion enter into the considerations. A review of the literature on automation quickly reveals that few, if any, "value free" discussions of the social impacts of the automation process are to be found. There seem to be hawks and doves abounding in this field. The hawks, infected with a violent technophobia, predict imminent and dire disaster as a result of the automation process. To support their point of view they marshall statistics and quote history.[1] On the other side of the question are the technophiles, or the doves, who predict that no noticeable change will take place in the organization of society outside of a salubrious rise in the level of productivity and a consequent elevation of the level of consumption.[2] The writer of this paper will occupy a position somewhere between these two extremes and might be called a pigeon, since he will no doubt lose feathers from each wing.

It seems that the opposing viewpoints of the hawks and doves may be reconciled if three questions were to be answered concerning automation before a position is taken concerning its ultimate effects on society. These questions are as follows:

---

1. References are listed at the end of the chapter.

1. "How is automation related to other parts of the technology of society?"
2. "How is technology in general related to the social organization of a society?"
3. "What kind of time perspective should we take towards technological change?"

Before conjuring up images of what society will look like in the future as a result of the automation process, we will attempt to deal with each of these three questions.

Automation and Technology

Technology consists of a system of strategies and tactics for producing desired end products through the use of human action augumented by tools and machines. Given this definition, it is apparent that all areas of human life involve technologies. There are, therefore, educational technologies, religious technologies, recreational technologies, technologies for family life as well as those normally thought of in the area of economic production, consumption and distribution.

Technologies combine an interlocking system of human action with the use of various agencies or instruments through which men act upon their environment and upon each other in the pursuit of goals or in the production of various kinds of products, both tangible and intangible. Technology, therefore, consists of a system of implements on the one hand and a system of human organization on the other. These two aspects of technology are so intimately intertwined that they are meaningless, one without the other. The implements (which for purposes of discussion can be classified as falling into three categories: (a) hand tools, (b) man-operated machines; and (c) self-operated machines) are distributed according to an organizational plan which matches implements with people and both with functions in a system of production.[3]

Automation, which we shall equate with self-operated machines or machine systems, must be viewed as part of this larger system of technology. Therefore, automation as a process must be viewed as being imbedded in a larger process of technological change. This larger technology involves a mixture of implement types varying from the hand tool to the self-operated machine on the one hand, and of sizes and shapes of human organizations on the other. The mix of implement types with organizational forms depends on the nature of the product being produced and on the limitations placed on technology by other factors which operate within the social system such as the values and beliefs that exist within that system.

Some products or goals lend themselves well to the use of self-operated or automated machinery, while others have qualities that make it difficult to reduce them to a machine technology much less an automated one. As a consequence, when we view the technology of society as a large complex system of subtechnologies, we will inevitably discover at the subtechnology level that some areas of society exist in the tool using or pre-tool using stage of development (religion and education), while other areas of technology (petrochemical industries) contain elements of automation existing alongside or necessarily with support of tool-using and man-operated machinery.

The automation process, which consists of the changeover in technology from the use of man-operated to self-operated or computer machine systems is a part of the larger social change process which has been going on in human society since its very inception. This social change process is a natural phenomenon which results from the operation of systems of interrelated causes or influences. Technologies are the creation of human behavior, and since human behavior itself is a natural phenomenon which is explainable in terms of a system of independent variables which combine to produce the behavior of human beings; then it follows that technology and its development are a part of a larger process which is explainable as a natural process.

Automation, then, is a part of what has been called socio-cultural evolution. In the long run of human history man has evolved various technologies through which he has satisfied his various needs and wants. The first technologies developed by human beings involved either manual manipulation of the environment or the use of crude tools. At a later stage in human development tools were combined to produce machines. Now we stand at a stage in the process of technological development or evolution when machines have become self-operating.

It is important to realize that within the total technology of society, at present, all of the forms of implements that have evolved over the long run of human history are still in use. Men still use their hands, tools, and machines as well as self-operated machines in intricate systems of technology which themselves are instruments for producing the products and services and for performing the functions that men define as desirable.

At this point in time, therefore, technology could be described as extremely elongated. By elongated, we mean that at one extreme are technologies based on the operation of the human organism as a thinking and acting mechanism unaided at times by even simple tools. At the other extreme, we have in existence systems of production which combine sophisticated computers with intricate systems of machines. Even in the most advanced society, this statement holds true.

When we view the larger picture of the entire world of man, technology becomes even more elongated stretching from the most primitive to the most modern. Most of the behavior of human beings in pursuit of goals or in the production of desired end products is still in the premachine stage of technological development. In most of the world, family life, religion, education, agricultural production, government and recreation, and for the most part the production of goods and services, are carried on with a premechanized or premachine technology. We must recognize, therefore, that by viewing man from a world perspective there exists side by side the most primitive and the most sophisticated technological schemes.

One of the questions that needs to be answered is whether there shall ever be a stage reached at which this elongation of technology will be reduced, and most or all of human productive activities will be carried on through the utilization of self-operated machinery. This question will be discussed in later paragraphs.

Technology and Social Organizations

The point has been made that automation is part of the process of technological development and change that has been going on since the beginning of human society. This process has changed the way in which men organize themselves to produce the various goods and services and institutional functions that are necessary to maintaining life in society. Since technology is a part of society, it is a truism to say that changes in technology change society. The question of whether automation will change the social organization of human social systems is likewise a question that calls for a truism as an answer, since automation is used in conjunction with human social organization to form technological systems.

Insofar as automation calls for a change in the distribution of personnel in society and in the roles that they perform, it will inevitably change society; or closer to the point, since automation refers to a way of organizing man machine systems and since it represents a change from other conceivable ways of organizing such systems, it amounts to social change.[4] The debate over the impact of automation on society is not a debate over whether or not it will affect social organization, but over how it will affect it. It will, therefore, be more instructive in this discussion to inquire into four questions:

1. How much effect will automation have on the social organization of society?
2. How long will it take for this effect to be realized?
3. In what parts of society will the effect be felt to the greatest extent?
4. Once automation has reached its climax and adaptive social change has occurred, what will society be like?

It seems apparent, as of this date, that automation has not progressed very far in our society. Only a small proportion of the goods and services now being produced by Americans are produced by automated systems. Most authorities who have bothered to look into the extent of automation agree that the process has moved very slowly to the present, and that the alarms raised over its impending effects on society have been, to say the least, premature.[5] A good case can be made at present for saying that the creation of automated production systems has resulted in small and temporary displacement of the labor force and, perhaps, has created more jobs than it has destroyed.

If we are to judge from the rate of change to automated systems which has so far been observed, the time period required to complete the automation process will be quite long. Compared to the predictions of the hawks or technophobiacs who predict imminent and dire disaster as a result of rapid and overwhelming automation the facts seem pale and uninteresting.

Economists, industrialists and businessmen all point to the fact that the costs of automating a production system are quite high and, therefore, pure cost considerations alone rule out rapid transition from man-operated systems to machine-operated systems in many cases. In addition to this, the inertia of ignorance of the possibilities of automation and the lack of "know-how" in moving towards it, and sometimes sheer prejudice against it on the part of managers as well as workers, seem to be slowing down the process to a "snail's pace." It seems apparent to this writer that 75 to 100 years will elapse before most of the production processes that lend themselves economically and technologically to the use of automation will have been automated. Furthermore, it seems apparent that certain areas of human activity aimed at the production of goods and services will remain in the pre-automation stage indefinitely into the future.

Determinants of Automation

In order to predict the rate at which automation will take place and the parts of society that will be affected by it, it is necessary to take into account certain facts about our present state of social organization. Within the culture of our society there exist certain values and beliefs that act as stimuli for furthering the automation process through fostering technological development in general. Side by side with these values and beliefs, there exist others that act as deterents to technological advancement, especially insofar as the development of automation is concerned. In other words, within our general value system, there exist conflicting values which act as motivating and deterring factors in the development of automation. On the motivating side are values such as the following:

1. There is a high value placed on efficiency in the production process in American society.

2. Americans believe strongly in the production of more goods and services as a way of increasing the general social welfare.

3. Americans believe that the profit motive tied to the competitive enterprise system acts to force the realization of efficiency on the one hand, and the productivity value on the other.

4. There is a high value placed on safety, health, cleanliness, etc., in the work situation in American society.

These and other values support the notion that greater automation is a desirable development to foster within society. It certainly can be argued that automated systems are more efficient in production than nonautomated systems. Likewise, it can be argued that they can produce more goods per unit of labor than other systems. Since they reduce the amount of labor necessary, they can operate on a more continuous schedule and thus produce more goods. It can similarly be argued that by cutting waste and labor costs, and by controlling quality and increasing output, automation satisfies the profit motive. Similarly, domestic competition and competition with foreign industry exert pressure in the direction of using automated systems as a means of achieving the other values stated.

Strong arguments can also be made in favor of automation as a means of improving safety in hazardous production processes, eliminating hazards to health and doing away with unpleasant working environments for human beings. Thus, these values and many others held by Americans and by persons from Western society in general form a powerful intellectual and moral motivation towards automation.

Perhaps more important than the values themselves is the fact that industrial enterprises, as they are now organized in relation to the mass markets at home and abroad, are forced by the pressures of competition and the desire (need) for a profit to continually improve the technological process. Since automation represents the highest development of technological process in society; it is inevitable, in the long run, that industry will move in its direction.

While there are strong values in society that act as motivating forces towards automation, there exist side by side with these other values that work against it as deterrents. Three among these will be singled out for attention.

1. There is a value in American society placed on full employment in the labor force. Americans hold that an adult male who is not physically or mentally disabled should work for a living and contribute to the productive system of his society.

2. Americans believe that a man's moral fiber and character is developed through work and destroyed by indolence and leisure. It is further believed, that if a person receives income without a just claim upon it through his labor, that he will be demoralized by the process.

3. A third belief exists that machines and computers dehumanize life and threaten to make slaves of men.

On the basis of these three values or beliefs rests the great concern over the long run of effects of automation. It is believed that automation, or technological development in general, will have the effect of reducing the opportunities for men to work by eliminating jobs, and that this will have the effect of creating a class of people who are perpetually the subjects of public welfare. Using the current model of the way in which public welfare works, an image is conjured up of a large class of jobless individuals who live on the "edge of subsistence" demoralized by being simultaneously powerless and on the public dole. On the other hand, the image is created of those who are working being slavishly tied to machines that control their lives and convert human beings into numbers in a giant technological conspiracy against mankind. On the basis of these beliefs, men oppose the introduction of technological advancements into various production processes in society.

It is likely that the existence of these two opposing sets of values will result in considerable conflict between segments of society as the automation process progresses. As a result of this conflict, the automation process will be slowed but eventually fulfilled since the power structure of society is organized in a way to favor the ultimate completion of the automation process.

In the heat of argument over how automation will affect society and as indignant debates proceed from firmly entrenched but conflicting values, more interest is displayed in lining up one's forces in favor of or against the process of technological development rather than in cooly evaluating the long run of effects of such a process on society.

Despite the debate, however, certain things seem, at this point, to be evident and beyond debate:

1. Automation is an existing part of the technological system of our society. It is an idea, an ingenious idea, about how to combine men, computers and machines into production systems. Such ideas are not easily suppressed, but rather tend to catch the imagination of men and shape their actions.

2. At present, automation represents only a small part of the total technology. This small part, however, proves the usefulness of the idea and serves as a living demonstration of the possibilities for future accomplishment.

3. Automated production systems use fewer workers to

produce a given volume of output than nonautomated systems do. Despite the desire of its advocates to allay the fears of the public over the possible unemployment effects of automation, its whole raison d'etre is tied up in replacing human agents by automatic systems. Only an ostrich could miss this point.

4. The cost of automating is high and, therefore, the rate at which it will be introduced into industry will be slow. For a long time it will be cheaper to employ human operators than to automate many kinds of production systems. Besides that, heavy investments are tied up in nonautomated systems.

5. When and if the production system of our society is fully automated, the number of people actively employed in economic production measured in terms of today's standards will be quite small, and the volume of production quite large.

6. To accommodate these facts the total pattern of human activity in society, and consequently the total social organization of society, has to be drastically different than it is today.

In the following paragraphs, let us speculate about how society will be changed at that distant day when the technological processes of automation have been extended to their fullest in the social system. It seems pointless at this time to argue the day-by-day effects of a process that is moving slowly as men see time. It might, however, be quite instructive to speculate about how society will look if we attain, through gradual day-by-day small changes in the organization of our technology, a state of maximum automation.

The image of the future which will be projected here is based on the following set of assumptions about how societies change.

Changes in society in response to automation will represent elaborations and extensions of already established trends and directions in society. This proposition is based on the notion that social changes usually come in small increments. An automated system is introduced into one part of one production process in society. In other parts of the production system of society, other small automation devices are introduced. Through the cumulation of this process, rather than through a radical change in the whole system, the technology of the society will develop towards automation. Similarly, adaptations in the social organization of society will come in small adjustments to the small changes taking place in the technological system of that society. Men will adapt their activity patterns and their institutions piece by piece through the making of thousands upon thousands of small decisions and small adaptations rather than through revolutionary changes in the social order. These thousands upon thousands of small changes in technology and adaptations in the social organization of society which are made separately will add up to what will appear over the long period of time to be major changes in social organization. They will, however, rest upon long established trends or directions of change and will present elaborations of patterns already existing in 1968 in the structure and organization of American society.

Current Social Trends

It has been pointed out that the direction that technological development will take and the consequent social changes that will emerge in society will, in all likelihood, represent elaborations on themes which already exist within American society. It might be well, therefore, to take stock of where we stand with respect to the impact of technological development in our society at the present moment before attempting predictions of things to come. There are a number of interrelated phenomena which are present in our society today that seem to be directly or indirectly associated with the current state of technological development and its history over the past several decades.

First among these is the fact that the amount of time spent by average individuals in work activities is at its lowest point in the history of our civilization. Over the past century, the work day and the work week have been substantially reduced. Along side of this has emerged a trend towards later entrance into the labor force with the virtual elimination of child labor, and earlier retirement. The work life of the individual as well as the work day and week has, therefore, shrunk considerably.

While it can be argued on the basis of solid evidence that unemployment in 1968 is at or near its lowest level in the history of our society, it is also true that the amount of time that the average individual spends working has been reduced. It seems likely that this trend towards shorter working hours, longer vacations, earlier retirement, and later entrance into the work force will shrink the work life of the individual to an even greater extent in the future.

This shrinkage in the work life of the individual cannot be attributed to automation. This technological development has not as yet had sufficient time to affect the distribution of work in society significantly. It has been the result of the development of mechanization in industry, agriculture, and commerce and of the consequent development of new culturally accepted definitions or norms of what the expected work career of the individual is that have been responsible for this trend. At the same time that this trend has been occurring in the world of economic employment, similar shrinkage in the amount of time spent in labor has occurred in the home. Housewives and children spend a smaller proportion of their time engaged in productive tasks in relation to maintaining the family than at any time in the past. In other words, throughout the society, the amount of time the average individual spends in so-called work or occupational activities has been drastically reduced. This has come about through mechanization without the impact of extensive automation as yet being felt.

While this reduction in the amount of work has been taking place, an astounding increase in productivity per man hour has occurred. The output of industry, of consumable products and services has reached an unprecedented level. Again this level of productivity has been achieved largely through the mechanization and increasing rationalization of production processes, and cannot be attributed to any large extent to the introduction of automation into production systems.

While these trends have been occurring in society, a general rise in the level of living enjoyed by the average member of society has been experienced. Nevertheless, large numbers of individuals live at so-called poverty levels near the border of subsistence. It is often pointed out in connection with this fact that our industrial plant and our agricultural technology is capable of producing even more goods and services than are now being produced without a major change in technology, and without increased investment in capital equipment. We are told that we are able to produce more steel given the present industrial plant than we now produce. It seems apparent that we are capable also of turning out more automobiles, washing machines, television sets, clothing and certainly more food given our present state of technological development and our present state of capital investment than we are producing at the moment. These observations lead to the oft-times cited paradox that we exist in a society capable of producing more goods than are now being consumed, but at the same time individuals and families exist within the society who are in need of food, clothing, shelter and other economic goods.

Leaving aside any argument over whether our present productive capacity would be capable of satisfying all or even a major portion of the potential wants of all of the people without further investment, it seems apparent to "hawk and dove alike" that we could achieve a more equitable distribution of our economic output if we are able to solve various problems of social organization that determine the distribution of goods and services within our society.

Our social order is founded on the proposition that a man's right to consume the products of the technological system of his society is established through the role he performs in the productive process, broadly speaking. The more important the role that he performs, the greater share in the consumption of the outpourings of the technological system he is entitled to. Carried to its extreme this proposition leads to the logical conclusion that if a person performs no role in the production process, as it is defined by members of society, he has no right to consume. Other values, however, exist within our society that mitigate the harshness of this formula and lead to programs of public welfare which provide at least minimum subsistence for persons who have no "legitimate role" in the production process. These programs base claims on consumption on humanitarian values rather than on role in the productive process.

In seeking to solve the poverty problem in our society, the answer which has most often been given is consistent with a dominant theme which states that the role in production measures the right to consume. It is usual to answer this question by saying that we should seek to achieve full employment — that every person in society who is physically and mentally able to work should be provided a job and, therefore, a role in the productive process. By so doing, we can establish that person's claim to consume the fruits of the economic system without altering our values on the one hand and our social organization on the other. Thus, public policy is aimed towards achieving full employment through the creation of new jobs, and new economic opportunities for work. These thoughts at least represent what appear to be the majority sentiment in American society and summarize the salient aspects of current public policy.

There are, however, disturbing stirrings in the social order.[6] The rise of groups within society who have a different perspective towards the economic and social order is a fact of our times. These groups challenge the basic tenets of the society and are apt to point an accusing finger in a direction of those who hold traditional values, pursue traditional goals and feel traditional motivations. The major sources of these dissident notes in the buzzing harmony of our industrialized social order come from the youth of the nation who have not yet entered the labor force, from the poor, especially the black poor who through circumstances have been locked out, and from intellectuals who by the nature of their roles are detached from it. It is no wonder that the loudest cries and protest against technological development come from these sources. It is not surprising that the largest number of technophobiacs are found among the ranks of the poor, the young, and the professional thinkers.

Let us examine the position of youth in relation to the technology of our society. A strong case can be made for saying that the present rebellious generation of college students represent the first class of individuals in society who have experienced, for a lifetime, the new affluence and the new leisure created by the technological developments of the past century. Prior to this generation, most youths experienced work as a part of life and similarly experienced deprivation, at least in a mild form as part of their membership in their society. The present generation of college students and those that will follow, however, have experienced a different world. They know it is possible to consume without being actively employed in the production process. Their consumption has for a lifetime been based on a "right" rather than a "role." They know also that consumption, when taken for granted at least, does not create a utopian state of existence whether one earns the right through work or is born with it. At the same time they are acutely aware of the fact that they live in the society that contains people who do not share in their taken-for-granted level of consumption. The right of children and youth to consume is obviously unequally distributed. Furthermore, no truly rational argument can be made to justify this inequality. The only arguments that can be made amount to saying that this is the way things are, or that is the way the system is organized. This leads the disaffected youth simultaneously to challenge the basic values of society and its organization and to desire to remake the social order in a different image. They propose new values and new ways of ordering things basing their approach on the assumption that society is a flexible instrument for attaining human ends and may be changed to suit new purposes without destroying old levels of production and consumption.

The youthful new left seems, therefore, to be a result of certain technological developments which have created a new kind of condition for youth in society and which have led to a new way of looking at the relationship between role in the production process and the right to consume.

Change from Agriculture

The civil rights movement is also intimately intertwined with technological development. With respect to civil rights, a large segment of the population is seeking a new and more satisfying role in the world of work at a time when such roles are disappearing not due to the as yet infant automation process, but to simple or not so simple mechanization. This mechanization, curiously enough, has occurred in agriculture, not industry.

Major technological developments in agriculture have triggered major changes in the way work is organized in agricultural enterprises. It has resulted in major shifts in the ecological pattern of farming and has produced mass migration and social mobility.[7] Millions of black sharecroppers and tenant farmers and their families, along with millions of white marginal landowners and tenants, have been forced off the land and into cities and towns. There they have arrived without industrial skills seeking employment that will give them a right to consume – or perhaps to just subsist. Thus, technological development in agriculture, and especially its mechanization and reorganization on an industrial basis, has resulted in a mass movement of population and a consequent mass unemployment or underermployment problem. In the opinion of this writer, this set of circumstances has been the major force behind the civil rights movement. This movement has merely been articulated by civil rights leaders and organizations, and by public officials and public policy.

The results of technological change are, in other words, very much with us. These, however, cannot be attributed to automation or even to industry; but largely to agricultural development. It is a tragedy of our times that the civil rights movement is occurring at a time when we are achieving such high levels of mechanization in agriculture and industry and, therefore, face more than the usual difficulties in absorbing a large, untrained labor force into the productive process.

It seems to be hardly debatable that the youth movement on the one hand, and the civil rights movement on the other will have considerable impact on the future rate of mechanization in industry, and certainly on the future rate at which automation occurs. This statement is made on the assumption that we will continue to pursue a policy of seeking full employment in the society. In aiming our efforts towards this goal we will inevitable be forced to create jobs for human beings rather than roles for machines and automated systems in the production process.

The new left, which represents an alliance between middle and upper class youth, black beople and the intelligensia forming an uneasy and mutually suspicious triangle is trying to define a new set of values for the society which they see as solving our current dilemmas. These new values are based on a combination of myth and fact about the nature of society and the nature of technology in relation to it. Part of the mythology concerns itself with the role of machines and computers and of automation in production. It is built upon the belief that given the right way of organizing things, we are capable of producing sufficient goods and services to satisfy all significant and legitimate human needs in the forseeable future. Yet there is a dualism involved in the mythology of the new left, since there exists within the belief system a suspicion and distrust of machines and machine systems as being the major dehumanizing agents in society. Another part of the mythology relates to the notion of power structure and the functioning of the decision making processes of society. Here the power structure is visualized almost as if it were a gigantic machine grinding out decisions in a conspiracy to enslave human beings by tying them to a technological process which becomes an end in itself.

No matter whether these beliefs correspond in any way to fact, they nevertheless shape the attitudes and actions of a significant minority of people in our society and represent a significant wave of protest against technological development. In the future they may foreshadow a new time of troubles in the so-called industrial revolution, a time of slowing down rather than a time of technological advancement. Cries which are now raised by the new left are so multiple and confused that no single message can be distilled from them, unless it be the message that a new set of values suited better to our advanced state of technological development are being formed in our society.

Perhaps the new integrating values which may emerge from the dualism that exists in our society today will place a high value on total unemployment in society, rather than total employment. It can be argued that the point of technological development has always been to make life easier for men by eliminating more and more of the drudgery of life and producing more and more goods at a smaller cost in human labor. It seems legitimate to many people, therefore, to direct human effort towards eliminating the necessity of work as fast as possible. This could be done through the rapid development of new and expanded systems of automation. Instead of attempting to create more work for human beings to perform so that they can have a claim to consume the products of the technological order, it would be more rational to direct our efforts towards attempting to produce goods and services with a minimum of human labor. This could be done not out of the profit motive but out of new humanitarian motives. We might pursue the automation process as rapidly as possible and invest our current energies to a greater extent towards producing more self-operated machine systems so that human beings can be released more and more from the necessity to be employed in order to have a right to consume.

It seems likely, however, that even in the most Utopian of Utopias where technology has advanced fantastically past its current state of development the necessity for work or employment will still exist. However, it is possible through shortening the work life and the work day and the work year of the individual to increase the amount of leisure through introducing greater and greater efficiencies in the production of goods and services, and at the same time to eliminate most of the boring routine of enervating tasks from existence.

The big problem in pursuing the goal of reducing human employment, and thus, the necessity to work through a deliberate process of mechanization and automation is the problem of establishing the right to consume the products of the economic system without simultaneously destroying the motivational system that is now attached to our system of distribution.[8]

As already pointed out, the primary basis upon which we base consumption rights, at present, is income derived from a work role performed in the production of goods and services. By gearing consumption rights to the role performed in the production process, a system for motivating people to work is also provided. The secondary basis for a right to consume is a dependency relationship to some individual who has income derived from a work role. Thus, wives, children, dependent relatives and other "wards" derive their consumption indirectly from a right established by another person's role in economic production. Through creating dependency relationships and through attaching certain rights and duties to the relationship between provider and dependent, an additional source of motivation to work is provided.

Men are led by the norms and values of their society to fulfill an obligation to provide for their dependents. Virtually, the only avenue for accomplishing this, left open by the structure of society, is a work role in the economic system. Thus men are supplied with additional motivation to work. The tertiary basis for a consumption right in our society lies in a status of ward to the state or to some other corporate group. Here the right to consume is based on the inability of a person to provide for himself due to special incapacities such as orphanhood, illness, physical and mental incapacity, incarceration and so forth. The values of our society are such as to hold that being a living human, in and of itself, establishes the right of the person to at least subsistence.

If all-out efforts were made to foster as rapid automation

as possible in all areas of human technology, it is apparent that the number of people whose primary basis for claiming a share in the output of the economic system would be reduced and, therefore, the rights of persons claiming a share on the secondary basis would be threatened. This could only mean an expansion in persons falling into the third category or the invention of still other categories of people whose right to consumption derives from a new and different source.

It has already been pointed out, however, that it seems inconceivable, even under twenty-fifth century conditions, for all work roles to be done away with through the mechanization process. This means that, at best, fewer people will have to perform work roles and more people will have to stand in one of the other dependency relationships to have a right to consume. Given this condition, it becomes a significant question to ask "how this minority of workers will be motivated to perform their work roles?" Similarly, it becomes significant to ask "how will society select the minority of workers from the total population?" Will they represent simultaneously an elite and a serfdom to the remainder of society? In some respects male members of our society today, between the ages of 21 and 60, represents the kind of minority that may be expected in the future.

The enormous difficulties involved in finding a basis for distributing the products of the economic system, which is radically different from our present basis for organizing distribution and consumption and the accompanying problems of maintaining motivation and selecting persons for work roles virtually rule out pursuing the more rational and appealing course of promoting rapid and complete automation so as to reduce the necessity to work in society. There are simply too many facets of our present value system, of the human being, and of the way our society is organized that would have to be changed before such a policy could be pursued effectively. This means that mechanization and automation must inevitably proceed at a pace that will permit us to make the small step-by-step alterations in our values and in our social organization that will allow the social organization of society to adapt to increased mechanization and automation without the whole system coming "unglued" in the process. Mass technologically induced unemployment without compensating redefinitions of the right to consume, and without a new basis for motivating people to work would almost certainly threaten to break down our social order into a state of warring factions.

Those persons who believe that revolutionary or cataclysmic social change, produced by a state of deliberately induced anarchy, could lead to making the adjustments in social organization necessary to exploit our present capacity for technological development, make claims to understanding the intricacies in functioning of advanced societies that are totally unsupported by the present state of our knowledge of how societies operate. Even if the wisest and most humanitarian group of persons on earth were assembled to redesign our society along the most utopian lines, they would have to act largely on the basis of their beliefs, values, prejudices, and preferences rather than on scientifically reliable knowledge of how societies operate in order to even begin the task of redesigning the social order. Almost certainly, the design for society emerging from such deliberations would be based on dogma and myth rather than scientifically supported principles of social organization. It is probably true that out of such a process of deliberate planning, given our current state of ignorance of principles of social organization, would come more errors costing greater human deprivation and suffering than would occur by less deliberate but more halting processes of social adaptation.

Let there be no mistake, however, about the meaning of these statements. It is because we are so ignorant of the inner workings of social systems that we are in this predicament. We now know more about how to build rockets and computers, or more to the point, how to automate production processes, than we do about how to build human social systems and to keep them functioning to meet human needs. Because we do, we can deliberately set out to send men to the moon with reasonable assurance that we will succeed. However, we are so ignorant about the structure and functioning of society that we cannot, at present, set out to eliminate poverty, crime, or air polution, or to promote rapid but undamaging technological development with a reasonable assurance of success.

It is our ignorance of the inner workings of human society that forces us to choose between unguided, automatic, gradual adaptive change processes on the one hand or dogma guided deliberately controlled change processes on the other. Given our state of ignorance, we are forced either to gamble on age old laissez-faire adaptive processes in social systems as promising the best chance that the system will survive and prosper, or on following some new charismatic social philosopher whose knowledge of the nature and functioning of human society is faulty at best. Going on the basis of some, all or nothing, revolutionary plan that is not based on solid knowledge is about like Icarus setting out for the sun using his homemade wings of feathers and beeswax. Going on the basis of automatic uncontrolled change processes is like putting up the family plantation as a stake in a crap game in which the dice are loaded against us.

Given the state of our present social science knowledge of how societies operate, the best we can do is to forecast probable developments and anticipate some of the many problems that seem likely to accompany them. This should lead us to attempt to develop reliable scientific knowledge concerning these trends and forecasts so that, as time goes on, we may establish mastery over our own society as well as over our so-called natural environment.

This will give us a third option in forming social policy. The price human beings have always paid in the past for following the "invisible hand" of automatic social change or the "messianic route" to social adaptation has been an unwanted and unwarranted level of human suffering in the form of poverty, oppression, or conflict, and other forms of human degradation. These so-called "social problems" have been the "side effects" or "latent functions" of both guided and unguided change processes. Given the development of reliable scientific knowledge of the workings of human society, however, it is hoped that we can accomplish social change and adaptation without paying the age old price in human misery. Such a price was paid for the original industrial revolution. Similarly, a high price has been and is being paid today for realizing the benefits of the new agricultural revolution.

Images of the Future

In the following paragraphs some trends will be examined and forecasts made about what is likely to happen in the process of society adapting to mechanization and automation through the operation of unguided social change.

There are several interrelated directions that our society is likely to take in adjusting to the continued process of mechanization, and to the acceleration of the infant process of automation. These directions of change are already present in our society as trends at a beginning stage. As the velocity of technological change increases and its impact on society is felt more drastically, these trends will become more pronounced.

Instead of pursuing a policy of total unemployment in society or allowing unemployment to grow at an uncontrolled rate, our society is much more likely to move in the direction of shrinking the amount of work performed by the average worker. This is likely to occur by: 1. Increasing the age of entrance into the work force; 2. shortening the length of the work day; 3. shortening the length of the work week; 4. lowering the age at which retirement from the work force occurs; and 5. increasing the length of vacations.

In this manner, more people can be absorbed into the productive process without altering the basic values and beliefs contained in the culture of the society. Arguments can even be made in favor of increased efficiency through the utilization of this solution. For example, it can be argued that a shorter work day utilizes workers during a period of maximum energy and attentiveness and, therefore, productivity. By raising the entrance age into the labor force more time is available for training and education and, therefore, a more educated work force will be available. By pushing down the age of retirement, it can be argued that the men employed in industry will work during their most productive period of life when they are apt to make their maximum contribution to the productive process. Thus, strong arguments already found in the value system of society can be made for moving towards a smaller amount of time spent in actual work.

The effect of this shortening of the work life will be an increase in leisure. Other patterns in society must be elaborated in order to take up the slack time left over through such a solution to the "unemployment" problem created by mechanizing and automating. At the same time the products of industry must be made available for consumption by the entire population; not just the working population.

Consuming Without Producing

As pointed out, a large segment of the American population at present consumes the products of the economic system on the basis of a concept that they have "a right to consume" This right is not based on their own role in the production process. Children, young people, and housewives consume on this basis for example. In order to make this seem reasonable, our culture contains an elaborate set of rationalizations to justify the right of children to consume. For example, we maintain that they will have a future role in the production process and, therefore, have a right to consume while preparing for this role in society. We maintain that they have a right to share the fruits of their parents' labor and base their consumption on an indirect relationship to a role performed in the productive process. It is on this latter basis that we justify the higher level of consumption on the part of some children than on others.

It will be necessary, in the process of shrinking the work life of the individual, to extend the period of life prior to entrance into the labor force so that it covers more years during which this right to consume is granted to young people. It is likely that this period will be taken up by true and sham educational activities which are invented to occupy the time of youth during which they are being withheld from the labor force. Rationalizations that every person has a right to an education at the higher levels as well as the lower levels will become more elaborate and more generally accepted. In addition to this, the notion that the public bear the cost of such education through providing subsistence as well as tuition for students during this period of time will become more and more prevalent.

The current belief that education is an economic reward-worthy work role on the part of students and, therefore, is a legitimate basis for their right to consume will be elaborated, spread throughout society and accepted without question. Similarly, the widowed, the orphaned, the handicapped and the aged will find their right to consume the fruits of the economic system greatly expanded. The definitions of these classes of people will be expanded to include more individuals. The rights of the "technologically unemployed" to concumption will also be elaborated and expanded. In all likelihood such individuals will go back to school and enjoy a right to consume on this basis.

The rights of unemployed women to consume, which are now based on marital or kinship relationships are likely to undergo a major change. It is the prediction of this writer that instead of expanding the number of women who will be gainfully employed in the future, as the trend in the past seems to foreshadow, we will see a reversal of this trend and a return to the family support model for females. Womens' level of consumption then will be determined by their husband's or father's relationship to the economic production process. Elaborate philosophical value positions will be developed to justify this consumption on the basis of right rather than role. All of these trends will be accompanied by expansion of unemployment insurance and social security type programs supported by taxes, and G.I. Bill of Rights type educational support programs for the young and the technologically obsolete members of our society.

There are a number of roles that people perform in society for pay at present that do not contribute directly, or even indirectly, to the production of economic goods and services. Nevertheless, members of society recognize the rights of such individuals to an income and, therefore, to a share in the consumption of goods. This right is established on the basis of their role in other institutions in society rather than their role in economic production. For example, teachers, priests, artists, musicians, actors, athletes, and comedians receive incomes for a role they perform for pay. Such individuals do not contribute directly to the production of goods which are consumable by other people in society. Nevertheless, the society recognizes the value of the roles they perform and grants them a right to income and to consumption. It is likely that new categories of such people will be invented in the future, and that old categories will be considerably expanded. These occupations have been largely defined as services in the past. They are services, however, which are rewarded on the basis of a cultural concept that their roles are important and desirable rather than economic.

When automation expands and changes begin to accelerate in the social order, we will see an expansion of the number of persons not working in the production and distribution of agricultural and industrial goods. This will occur both by withholding large numbers of people from any form of employment in society and by expanding the categories of individuals whose work activity involve "nonproductive or noneconomic service activities."

The Elaboration of Nonproductive Activities in Society

If the amount of work time expended by the average individual in society is reduced drastically and at the same time a large number of individuals are withheld from participation in the production processes, it seems apparent that a large amount of time will be left over for human activities other than work. In order to fill the void, our society will have to elaborate considerably on already existing nonwork patterns and invent new ones. Some of these patterns will involve recognizable recreational activities. Others will involve new or expanded activity patterns which are neither recreation nor work. There are four categories of expansion in nonwork activities that seem likely in the future on the basis of what can be observed in society today. They represent directions that our society seems to be moving at present on the one hand and can be identified with major directions that historical societies have taken in the past when they reach a juncture similar to the one we are now facing.

The Narcissistic and Sensate Trends

The writer predicts that in the future a much greater amount of time will be spent by the average individual on narcissistic activities such as personal grooming, dress, bathing, plastic surgery, plastic dentistry, health maintenance, physical culture, and "cosmetic psychiatry." Trends in this direction have already developed in our society. People are paying much more attention to themselves as the object of their own activities than ever before. The mirror in the bathroom, the cosmetic and the deodorant, the dentist, the barber, the beautician, the reducing salon, and the clothier are all favorite focuses of attention for the young and not so young.

People are spending much more time in "taking care of themselves" and in projecting an image to others on the basis of some inward fascination with the self as an object. It is anticipated that much more of human activity will be contributed to the overt expression of such narcissism. As a consequence, industries associated with narcissistic activities will expand, and occupations in these areas will proliferate. Employment in this area will increase and shift some individuals away from areas of employment feeling the impact of automation and mechanization. The long hair and the fancy clothing with self aggrandizing pretentions so popular among certain segments of our population are an extreme expression of this trend.

Related to the marcissistic trend in society is a trend towards emphasizing the senses as a source of pleasure. Pitirim Sorokin held that societies vary between two stages in their development, an ideational stage and a sensate stage.[9] During the sensate stage they emphasize gratification of the senses and elaborate systems of human action aimed in this direction. It appears that our society is entering such a phase. The development of psychedellic drugs and their surrounding patterns of art and music as well as the orgiastic organization of hippie communities with their emphasis on the happening, point in the direction of such a development. It is not, however, the hippie alone who is moving in this direction. Food, music, art, sports, sex, drink and drugs find popularity expanding within the general population of society. In the future, it is likely that this emphasis on gratification of the senses will increase and the number of people engaged in sensate types of occupations will expand.

The number of participaters in society who utilize major amounts of their time in gratifying the senses will also expand. This trend could result in a new blossoming of the graphic and performing arts and music in our society. Infant trends in these directions can be seen at present as people begin to question the quality of life in our society. This trend towards the development of the arts is at present growing by leaps and bounds in a society glutted with goods but relatively poor in artistic sophistication.

Ideational Trend

Sorokin saw the ideational phase in society as one devoted to the development of ideas. It is the contention of the present writer that our society is seeing the simultaneous burgeoning of both the ideational and sensate directions in society. The growth of concern over the philosophical matters displayed by the hippie community and the youth of our society goes on side by side with experimentation in the sensate possibilities of our new technology. The young and old alike are concerned with matters of religion, philosophy, the growth of science and with political ideas. We are in the process of experimenting in the realm of the mind as men have never experimented before. We may, in other words, be turning in the same direction that ancient Greece turned when their immediate problems of an economic nature seemed temporarily to have been solved rather than in the Roman direction, which was essentially sensate in nature. This ideational development could find expression in the foundation of new religions and in the reinvigoration of old ones. We may see the multiplication of religious, philosophical and political cults; especially those that combine an intellectual rationalization with a sensate mode of expression.

The so-called new politics, existential philosophy and hippie culture along with its ideational drug taking and mind expanding philosophy, represent the beginning stages of a trend in this direction. Such activities can take up the time of a lot of people left over from the production process, and at the same time expand work activities for others. In so doing no aggravating contribution to the surplus of goods already presenting a problem will be made.

The Monumental Trend

It is conceivable that our society will turn more and more to producing monumental structures and holding spectacular events. Bigger buildings, larger highways, more stadiums, and perhaps even larger tombs to commemorate the narcissistic dead may be in our future. In other words, our society may turn in the direction of expending its energies much as the ancient Egyptians did to commemorate the self, or to commemorate the ideational and sensate heroes of our era, or the ideational and sensate institutions of our times. On this basis, churches and temples might grow in size and splendor as they did in the Middle Ages. The halls of government may be elaborated and expanded to commemorate the ego of both their creators and their users. The stadiums in which sporting events are carried on might grow in size and splendor, and the homes in which people live may be elaborated beyond our present conception of the stage upon which the family drama is played. In other words, a kind of monumentalism in the building of the physical setting within which human activity takes place might be forthcoming in the future.

Conspicuous Waste

It is probable that the present trend towards more and more disposability of objects in our society will be extended. Disposable clothing, cooking utensils, food, bottles, and more readily disposable automobiles, houses, and other objects seem to be in our future. This will allow us to waste the products of our productive system conspicuously and rapidly so that there is a steady flow of goods from the production line to the scrap heap. This, of course, will keep the mills of industry turning and at the same time reduce the necessity of performing certain types of labor in the home or in other places of the society. It will, of course, present a monumental problem for the garbage and trash collectors of the society, but this will no doubt be solved by using disposable disposals.

Some Structural Consequences

Continued technological development will result in certain structural changes in society. These changes are already under way and are, therefore, readily recognizable. The first is a trend toward giantism in the organizations that comprise society. The size of future economic enterprises will far exceed their present scale and reach a truly mammouth size. Such growth in size is inevitable if the investments necessary to complete the mechanization and automation processes are to be made.

The scale of these gigantic organizations will be measured in terms of their capital investment, and in terms of their output rather than in terms of employees. They will grow in size as measured in these terms while the number of employees remains stable or drops in number. This trend can be recognized today in the petrochemical industry where automation is more nearly complete than in other parts of society.

Growth in scale of government can be expected to parallel growth in organizations in the private sector. The so-called public sector will have to assume more and more of the burden of maintaining and promoting the public welfare as society shifts from "full employment" to a "partial employment" basis. This will occur as the distribution and consumption problems fostered by technological development emerge. The rapidly increasing population which will be supported by the benefits of advancement in technology will also place pressures toward expansion in government. The increased population of cities and states as well as the nation will create the need for a larger scale in governmental organization to meet the needs of the public.

Because of the nature of the social and economic problems associated with advancement in technology, government and private enterprise will be forced to form consortiums to meet exigencies of the emerging problems created by technological development. Such consortiums will resemble in form those between government and private enterprise in the atomic energy field and in space exploration. Such patterns are already being experimented with in the poverty area and in education. To the sociologist, whose interest is in the real structure of society rather than in the myths of its structure, it will become increasingly difficult to discover where government begins and private enterprise ends.

In the face of such size and complexity in organization; the average individual, in the future, will feel more helpless than he does today when he attempts to relate to either government or industry. Because of the bureaucratic nature of both governmental and private organizations, power in society will become more concentrated in the hands of a few individuals who have enormous responsibilities for keeping the system operating. These individuals, while possessing great power, will themselves feel relatively powerless to control the giant systems that they head. These systems will themselves be so large and complex that the men at the top will have difficulty in directing them in the directions they desire.

In the process of technological change, the power structure of society will change. Economic and political power will shift away from some industries and institutions toward others. Such shifts are already noticeable. There was a time not long ago, for example, when the men who owned or controlled the railroads and the steel mills were the dominant power figures on the economic and political stage. Today power has shifted towards the electronics, petrochemical and aerospace industries. The future will see more such shifts in power away from traditionally dominant interests in society toward new and emerging interests.

Because of the particular problems of technological change, labor unions and educational institutions will achieve new positions of power in the future. Unions will gain renewed influence as the anxiety of workers over a real or imaginary lost job security emerges out of the technological change process. Educational institutions will gain increased power as they engage in research and training designed to ameliorate the various problems growing out of technological development, and as more people spend greater amounts of their time as students in various forms of educational organizations.

Warfare, Foreign Aid and Space

The point is often made that our excess of production over consumption, given the limitations of our domestic system for distributing goods and services, is now being funneled off into warfare, foreign aid and space exploration. It is held that these activities are necessary to keep the economy growing since we are unable or unwilling through other means to utilize the full production of industry for domestic peaceful consumption. It is terribly difficult to counter this argument in a society that contains the amount of poverty that is present in ours.

On this basis as well as on other ideological grounds the new left has opposed the military establishment and the war in Viet Nam. On this same basis millions of persons who perceive themselves as economically deprived question the wisdom of foreign aid expenditures and expenditures for space exploration.

Whatever can be said about the merits of military programs, foreign aid, and space exploration on both practical and ideological grounds, it seems to be apparent that our economy would be sorely taxed to distribute the products of industry were governmental expenditures in these fields discontinued suddenly.

One direction that our society could go in the future could be in the direction of increasing activities of this sort so as to provide a continuous escape valve for our excess of productivity over the domestic, nonmilitary capacity to consume.

The exploration of inner and outer space provide particularly fertile fields for accomplishing such a purpose. For one thing, space hardware is fabricated by the opposite kind of productive process from automation. Such hardware is virtually hand made, and because of the necessity for great precision and reliability requires fantastic amounts of human labor in testing and inspection activities. Furthermore, even though space craft and their launching, monitoring and recovery systems are largely automated, they require large crews of highly trained and highly paid experts to design and operate them. Thus they present an example of how automation and technological development has created a whole system of new occupations and jobs, which themselves do not produce consumable goods but create purchasing power for such goods in society. It is well to note that such enterprises are almost totally dependent on tax money for their support. Through them, using taxation, purchasing power is distributed to persons employed in, essentially, a noneconomic enterprise.

The future of foreign aid and of military activities is the most difficult of all trends in our society to unravel at the moment. This is because they force us to think in global terms rather than in national terms and thus force us to attempt to face problems of world technological development and change. Several facts seem apparent in this field against which all forecasts of the future must be made. First, virtually every nation of the world is, in one form or another, attempting to promote technological development and industrialization. While some are moving rapidly (Russia, Japan and Italy) and others are moving slowly (African and Southeast Asian countries), all are oriented toward modernizing their exonomic system through industrialization, mechanization and automation.

Second, the size of the population of almost all nations of

the world is increasing. This means that the size of markets are increasing and the demand for raw materials is growing by leaps and bounds.

Third, no single nation of the world seems to possess the richness in raw materials necessary to meet the potential needs of its developing economy from domestic sources.

Fourth, given enough time to mechanize production and access to enough raw materials there could be many nations in the future able to produce more industrial products than their domestic population could consume.

These facts seem to point to sharper competition among nations for both markets and sources of raw materials in the future. In the past such competition has been a major source of armed conflict and the ultimate domination of one nation by another. Today, however, open warfare is too dangerous among the powers actually competing for markets and raw materials since atomic warfare could destroy the entire society and make the conflict meaningless. This means that the conflict over markets and sources of raw materials must be fought out on a different basis than in the past.

What seems to be emerging as the solution to the problems of international economic relations is a new form of super-national enterprise system. Business and industrial firms are spilling past national boundaries and a rapid interpenetration of national productive systems is occurring. This is being promoted by foreign investments from private sources, and by foreign aid and the technological advisor systems promoted by governments. Nations are being tied to each other by super organizations that transcend national boundaries in both directions. This trend is observable in both the Eastern and Western blocs of nations. The so-called uncommitted nations are being courted from both sides and are being pushed slowly but surely, as the price for industrializing, to commit themselves to one or the other of the two blocs.

This interpenetration of nations in both the private and public sectors of economic development is far more significant for the organization of the world of the future than the brush fire wars that are taking place in those areas where neither bloc has established a significant beachhead in this manner. They are also far more significant than the existence of the United Nations as an international organization.

Military expenditures in the future, as now, will be primarily based on the overwhelming fact that the world is slowly moving politically and economically towards being organized into two supernations with supernational economic systems based on supernational organizations. Given this diagnosis of the future, it seems difficult to envision a lowering of military expenditures for the defense of these supernations in the near future. The organizational penetration is taking place within but not between these blocs. Therefore, it is likely that in both large blocs of nations, military expenditures will remain high for a long time to come.

Because we are moving toward a supernational economic and political structure, it likewise seems improbable that foreign aid expenditures and foreign investment of private capital will significantly decrease. However, increased productive capacity in other nations as well as our own and a similar movement at different rates towards automation will transform our current dilemma over how best to use our industrial plant to satisfy human needs to the level of an international problem.

REFERENCES

1. Jaques Ellul, *The Technological Society,* Alfred A. Knopf, New york, 1965; Norbert Weiner, *The Human Use of Human Beings,* Houghton Mifflin Co., Boston, 1950; *The Triple Revolution,* The Ad Hoc Committee on The Triple Revolution, Washington, D.C., 1964.

2. Charles E. Silberman, *The Myths of Automations,* Harper & Row, New York, 1966; George Terborgh, *The Automation Hysteria,* W.W. Norton & Co., Inc., New York, 1965.

3. For a discussion of the meaning of technology and its relationship to automation and social organization see: G.H. Amber and P.S. Amber, *Anatomy of Automation,* Prentice Hall, Inc., Englewood Cliffs, New Jersey, 1962, Chapter 1; Jacques Ellul, *op. cit.,* Chapter 1; Charles R. Dechert, *The Social Impact of Cybernetics,* Simon & Shuster, New York, 1967, Chapter by Robert Theobald.

4. *Technological Trends in Major American Industries,* Bulletin Number 1474, U.S. Department of Labor, Feb., 1966, pp. 1-9.

5. Roger W. Bolz, *Understanding Automation,* The Penton Publishing Co., Cleveland, Ohio, 1966, Terborgh, *op. cit.,* Silberman, *op. cit.*

6. *The Triple Revolution, op. cit.*

7. James H. Copp, *et. al., Our Changing Rural Society,* Iowa State University Press, Ames, Iowa, 1964.

8. *The Triple Revolution, op. cit.*

9. Pitirim Sorokin, *Social and Cultural Dynamics,* (4 Vols.), Bedminster Press, New York, 1962.

9

A Comforting Conclusion and Significant Alternatives

Chairman:

Robert Dubin

Deliberations on the Social Aspects of Automation

Robert Dubin, Research Professor, Department of Sociology, University of Oregon, earned an AB, AM and Ph.D, University of Chicago. Dr. Dubin is a Fellow of the American Sociological Association and has been a Senior Fulbright Research Fellow in England. He is an author whose studies have centered on industrial relations and management and is now editing the *Handbook of Industrial Sociology*.

How do we perceive the use of automation and technological development as an instrument of society or an instrument to be used by society to achieve whatever goals we may assume society has? Our perception of goals may be backward-looking rather than forward-looking. We're saying that the solution to our problem of poverty is fuller participation in employment in the production system. This has been the traditional solution of problems of level of living and improving the welfare of human beings in our society. Is this goal feasible and will this method be effective?

What role does automation bear in full employment if, indeed, that is a goal of our society? The elevator operator said, "Next year I will be a button; you press the button and it does my job." Automatic elevators have replaced vanishing operators. What has happened to the operators? Automation may provide the escape of people from drudgery. Automation generally requires a superior level of skill and people are becoming unautomated by automation.

Shall we evolve a society in which we can fulfill the needs of all of the people with a smaller percentage of the work force committed to actual production? If so, can an individual develop, from a psychological point of view, a creative or satisfying way of life that does not involve industrial work?

Can the Order Change?

One assumption underlying the process of technological development is that human wants increase indefinitely. As productivity increases, the number of different kinds of products and services that human beings desire also appear to increase. The conclusion is that human wants are insatiable. Society itself transmits to us the notion of what we want, what is desirable, how many things and what kind. Is it possible to change the values of society so that this particular insatiability of human beings involves a different order of things?

We still live in a society which generally finds work is good and one which derives satisfaction from most work and this is still a very powerful motivation. But, today there are people who have no such motivation and are unable to work for various reasons. It is one thing to be legitimately unemployed and another thing to be a victim of unfair or legally protected discrimination.

Clarification of the relationship between our unemployment problems and automation is needed. In industries that have automated — banks, insurance companies, communications, etc. — people that were already in productive processes remain and the number employed grows. Unemployment problems in the ghettos are not attributable to automation. In a sense our present unemployment problems are unrelated to automation.

Part of this problem is unwillingness to change. It is a sociological factor that is real and present. In one west coast plant where thousands were laid off — out of a sample of 100 — only 10 were willing to be trained for another kind of job. Resistance to change is probably the only critical sociological factor that arises with automation and unless society creates in younger people a willingness to change, the problem tomorrow will be worse than today.

Can We Choose Wisely?

This is a critical time in the development of our society. The problem is serious because clear perception of what is going on is clouded by the amazing diversity that confronts the viewer. Poverty and unemployment exist side by side in an environment of fantastic productive capacity. Efforts to cope with these problems may lead to solving problems left over from a previous stage of development — a backward step that may create much more difficult problems to solve, perhaps on an international rather than a national level. In other words, in seeking a solution through participation in the industrial economic system as the road to correcting poverty, injustice and inequality in society, we may actually be choosing to slow down changes imperative to attainment of a higher level of achievement in society for the future. A simplistic choice now may create more new kinds of problems in the future.

It may be that we have reached a level of population density and technological sophistication where automation becomes *the* essential answer to a number of things that have to be done and that we really can't do without. Perhaps we need to look on automation as a tool that society of necessity invents when it reaches a certain level of density and sophistication. Automation after all can be viewed simply as a tool, and everyone must realize that investment controls the pace of automation. Unless proper conditions prevail, no automation will materialize.

Much has been said about increased leisure but there are problems here. It comes back to the freedom of the individual which must not be abrogated regardless of circumstances. In all probability we should begin to reorient our thinking regarding the work role since already the majority of people in our society are engaged in services rather than in production. From the automation perspective this means that people at both ends of the talent spectrum are feeling the change and need to adjust their outlook. Some may feel a sense of frustration and inadequacy in competing for the new jobs. The sociological problem is to make it easier for these people to find the *right* place in society to fit in with a society that needs new and varied kinds of skills.

We must really face the issue of automation and society realistically. All automation promises is a much higher utilization of resources available to the nation. Available resources are therefore magnified many times. In a sense we can afford any type of society we want. What kind? Utopia, of course!

Perhaps we should visualize a serving society — a society that has learned a responsibility to man. And, to survive we must have a human-oriented society, a humanistic society, a society of service to man. But if we get a jobless society, we get society without roles. People identify with their role in society — with what they do. If we look forward to a society in which nobody has anything in particular to do in maintaining the bread and butter aspect, then we are looking for a society in which, as we are trained to see it, no one has a role. Our model is unreal if we look ahead to several hundred million people in the country with nothing to do — machines taking care of everything they need — operating their cities, their transportation, their communications.

New Directions

Management in the past several decades has come a long way in understanding the individual and trying to build into the job more opportunity for the individual to be productive for himself and for the organization as a whole; we still have a long way to go in this regard.

We have opportunities to be creative in considering alternative ways of utilizing time. Potentialities for self-development as well as social contributions appear to be enormous. There are many movements — educational and otherwise — designed to allow the individual to explore himself or his potentiality so time does not have to hang heavy on the person's ability to use it meaningfully. There is need to consider the problem of motivating people in this area of self development.

It will become increasingly important to involve children at a very early age in the environment around them as participants, not just consumers. If begun early enough it can be anticipated that young people will adapt easily to new roles in their community. The idealism of youth in a new constructive form of expression would result.

The problem, in this country, for some time to come is not merely going to be with the unemployable young. We have a temporary problem here, particular with some ethnic groups — but this will change and is changing. The pattern may shift to retired people and how they may continue to make significant social contributions. The mores of our employment practice discourage their involvement in activities which are income producing.

The problem of the young is somewhat similar. Over a million young people a year come out of school without having graduated. Over a million a year come out of school disaffected with the routine of life, and they aren't really absorbed into the labor market until they are about 26 years of age. It seems our institutions are not geared to let them get out into the work world at an earlier age.

Some Critical Questions

Do we face the matter of deciding who will consume what in our society? Why not give the so-called "hard-core" unemployed a decent income and not worry about whether they work for it? Perhaps one of our problems now is that we have too much inefficient labor in our productive system. Not using them may enhance our productive capability; and may be the cheapest solution in the long run.

Can man accept such an alternative? Do jobs provide human satisfactions which other roles cannot supplant? To what extent does a job define us as "in" rather than "out" from a societal point of view? Our institutions are operated to discourage a person from being without a job. There is a prevalent belief that people tend to feel useless and unwanted when they don't have an occupation as a part of society. This suggests that in order to have people who do not work, in the conventional sense, the whole ethic of society must be changed. This may be necessary. A segment of our society appears already to have thrown away that ethic, successfully, to their own satisfaction.

Is it permissable for society to pay people a basic fundamental living wage when they are born as a right of entrance into this world? Does that suggest that sometime in the future we establish criteria to determine who can be born into this world? Or does it imply that we give people board, room, clothing, transportation and so forth as a basic right because they are here? These are questions being asked.

The "world owes me a living" concept has become nontrivial. With guaranteed income, under some circumstances, unemployment may become the desired status for some individuals. The senior worker may claim seniority rights to be the first laid off and retreat to the back porch or the neighborhood club. Is this the modern image of the human nature of the contemporary working man? Do most people, indeed, seek to maximize enjoyment with minimum effort? If society provides opportunities for people to minimize effort and still get something which to them is satisfactory, are they going to do just that? We must know the answer.

There are some psychologists who would maintain that the only people who are really happy are those who are strongly committed to some sort of productive or creative effort, not necessarily for money, nonetheless some particular activity to which they are committed.

Productivity is usually associated with the notion of effort extended for pay. Is it, in the individual's philosophy, possible to change over to creativity, not necessarily labors for pay? Some people are now doing this voluntarily but, can we rationalize paying people for activities which we do not currently label employment? Do we have to change human nature or do we simply take advantage of human potentialities? One possible area in which to search for answers is in the study of how new careers are developing.

In industry this problem has been posed traditionally in the conflict of the needs of the individual and the needs of the organization. One solution has been to change the nature of the business environment to more successfully tap the potentialities of individuals. Wide participation of employees is possible without adverse effects on production or profits. There are similar opportunities in education, in politics and in the social environment.

A fundamental question concerns man's real purpose in a productive society. We can postulate that the purpose of life is really essentially to develop oneself in as many aspects as possible, in as many dimensions. This may be what life is all about. It is certainly not to produce a certain number of automobiles, not to achieve a certain level of income; really to live life as fully and completely as possible. This means, the sum total of human experience. If one would accept this and one would say that the individual normally and naturally would seek this type of self-realization, then the only question is can we allow him to do this in a way which satisfies himself and is not detrimental to the people around him?

As a society we must learn what the constraints on the individual have to be. We had to learn what they were for business; now we're in the process of having to learn the maximum range of liberty that can be allowed an individual in our society. That society works best which has maximum freedom, but only when accompanied by full responsibility.

Is it correct to assume that man is inherently intellectual? Is it correct to assume that most people would in the future, assuming we have the productivity to permit fewer hours of work, become interested in serving mankind or reading the literature of the ages? Automation provides the means for the good life, but its definition is an individual affair.

Hastening the processes of automation will increase the output of goods and services that American society is capable of producing and raise the general standard of living. The best for this society in the long run may be to increase our productivity and decrease the amount of work that has to go into doing this. The rub is that we are hung up on a value conflict.

We're making things automatically right now, and the consumer's hand is guiding what is going on and choices are being made. We're moving along a road that has certain points of "no return." Decisions being made now will determine how we live with automation and how far it goes.

If "conspicuous waste," as mentioned by Dr. Bates, is a concomitant of technological development, the concept may have an undeservedly bad reputation. To some, conspicuous waste is a positively functional aspect of our society. Conspicuous waste, it can be argued, has saved millions of man-hours. For example, not having to return untold numbers of bottles to the store and from the store to the processor, which takes up not only the returner's time but also the store clerk's time and delivery, may be regarded as a boon to mankind. Prepackaging has saved much time in food preparation in the home. The so-called conspicuous waste may have raised our standard of living tremendously. The point is, however, that conspicuous waste becomes the definition of the standard of living. Planned obsolescence or plain careless manufacture may more aptly describe the undesirable type of conspicuous consumption.

With Automation Matured

What sort of projection can we make for the future? Suppose in year 2000 we had achieved an automated society; our technology had reached a point where the achievement of the first industrial revolution, the conclusion or midstream of the second industrial revolution, the automation revolution was history. Assuming that automation is fully matured; what sort of society do we foresee? What sort of society is possible under conditions of mature industrial automation?

It would seem that the first and most obvious thing that can be said of society under conditions of maximum automation would be that the nature of employment in society and the extent of employment in industry will be radically different than it is now. There will be a smaller percentage of the population employed in industrial occupations and various other productive occupations for shorter periods of time. There will be dozens of different ways in which people in society will fill their time, when there has been release from much work activity. One direction is greater concern with self and its development. Another direction possibly is in terms of the satisfaction of the senses through new kinds of activities. Whatever the direction, it will represent a radical change in the patterns of activities of people in society.

Segments of society may have more work activity — not less; the managerial group for example. Today it seems that managers of organizations are increasing their work week and the pressures on them are becoming greater. The managers of big organizations may be busier in the year 2000 than they are today. Management itself, however, may become to a degree automated. Many managerial decisions lend themselves well to automation. Managerial skills involve the handling of information and we are developing information systems that can help make many of the decisions now made laboriously by man.

Automated or not, managerial decisions in the future will have to be made more quickly because of complex involvements and the consequences of the decisions. Automation will supplement, as it is doing now, the art of management to the extent that less time will be necessary and perhaps less anguish in the making of these important managerial decisions.

Conclusions Comforting

The degree of automation in our society in the year 2000 will probably be much less than our technical capability warrants. The process of automation will be less than totally complete because it will not be possible to alter society in the directions that will permit the completion of the process. Society is constructed in such a way as to slow down, impede and perhaps even prevent the utilization of some of these techniques that could be employed. An example is education — in the university. Here is a field that could utilize some automated techniques, but higher education is now organized in such a way that there will be great opposition to doing so. We may be unable to take advantage of the technical revolution because of these factors which are present in society. The society, now or in the future, which is able to change values or modify its social organization will be the society to fully develop the potentiality of technology.

If automation was a monopoly of the United States, it could be controlled by our government, our industry, our unions, or social pressures. But, now we see the whole world quite eager and where able, willing to automate. Japan, for example, has chosen to automate to a high degree. On the other hand, we sometimes automate only when forced into it. There is some evidence in some fields already that we must either automate or suffer a loss of market and jobs.

Just how all of these conflicting problems and interests will be resolved in the mature automated society will call for more realistic appraisal of facts, more study, and a deeper understanding of an extremely complex society.

Perhaps the Bateian world will ultimately appear, but there will be an intermediate world for which the developments in automation technology can provide promising solutions to pressing but manageable problems. In a way automation can be viewed as the necessary (and perhaps even miraculously appropriate) means for solving the emergent problems of the first industrial revolution. And, to many, it is comforting to note several essential factors in conclusion:

1. The perceived rate of change in industrial technology appears to be slow enough to be readily absorbed without shock.

2. The fruits of automation and its job creating potentials can be turned to the socially necessary task of putting the hard core to work and raising the level of living of the poor.

3. When our domestic house has been put in order with the aid of automation, there will still remain the task of aiding the rest of the world.

10

The Business/ Economic
Dimensions of Automation

Herbert S. Kleiman

Herbert S. Kleiman, Senior Economist, Department of Economics and Information Research, Battelle Memorial Institute, holds a BEE, The Cooper Union; MBA, New York Univeristy; DBA, The George Washington University. Has investigated various aspects of the changing electronic technology. Dr. Kleiman's major interest areas relate to the application of economic/business principles to technology-based companies. His writings and lectures have focused on technical-economic aspects of the electronics industry.

"Machinery will perform all work – automata will direct them. The only task of the human race will be to make love, study and be happy."

United States Review, 1853

Over 100 years since that Utopian forecast was ventured, we are still seeking the bliss implied by the ultimate in mechanization and automation. Certainly with great strides in automation since the antebellum period, one can argue indefinitely whether we are happier, more studious, or enjoy more time to make love. To assert that automation has been a mixed blessing is to repeat the obvious: the unparalleled U.S. standard of living, partly attributable to the automation phenomenon, is under attack for its selectiveness, its cost in human values and natural resources, and its apparent increasing indifference to those it serves. Whether the business/ industrial community responds to this censure in a positive fashion is questionable. History is not very encouraging, nor do more recent events offer much promise. If the desired changes are brought about, institutional innovation will probably be the activating mechanism rather than the volatile force of periodic public outcries.

As material wealth has accrued, the "have nots" within and without our national boundaries have levelled sharp criticism at our unique achievement. Many of today's realized and tomorrow's anticipated problems derive from our economic well-being: the headlines of any newspaper bear out this contention.

As we wrestle with the broader social questions, we also encounter other issues and other dimensions relating to business and industry. Even within strictly economic bounds, the long-term prospects for automation involve complications created by automation's own success. This dichotomy results from the cost shifts incurred as a production process evolves from a capital-intensive to a labor-intensive activity. The automation-unemployment debate, the movement of production facilities overseas, and the free trade-protectionism dispute are all variations of the same theme.

A Look at Key Aspects

Although the interrelationship between the social environment and business entities within carries great weight for the future, this paper will focus upon automation within the more direct business/industrial/economic context. And from the plethora of possibilities that even this narrowed-down subject area offers, I would like to concentrate* upon only a few items which I believe are less than obvious yet more than important to the long-term viability of automation as part of our industrial complex.

Automation will be instrumental in accelerating the dominance by a breed of business giants possessing increasing influence and control over our economic destinies.

The affinity for bigness appears to be all-consuming. Whether by merger in its many faces or internal growth, large size sometimes seems to be an end unto itself. How often do we read of a business marriage whose only rationale appears to lie in the arcane financial data or the promptings of a midwife financial organization? But the movement toward bigness predates the current trend; its roots trace back to the mid-1800's.

When the consumer satisfied many of his needs directly,

---

*See Appendix

when the supply/demand parameter was specified in only local terms, when the manufacturing-through-marketing functions were all housed under one roof, when the demand for products was fairly static, and when the multiplicity of those products was extremely limited by demand and supply — then the small business entity could survive and thrive. Toward the last third of the 18th century, these conditions were fast changing: the consumer and manufacturer were further apart, distances were now also measured in thousands rather than only hundreds of miles, urbanization was beginning its unrelenting siege, and the Civil War had proven that industry was the wave of the future. Bigness was not only desirable, it was necessary. The large organization could best accommodate a widely-based geographical demand, it could obtain the requisite financial support, it could afford to advertise its wares, and it could exert the economies of scale.

By the turn of the century, the "Robber Barons" and Big Business had caused enough disquiet to generate the Sherman Anti-Trust Act and to set the muckrakers off on their crusading tasks. By today's standards, the corporate targets of that era were pygmy-sized:

> In 1917 the asset value of U.S. Steel totalled $2.5 billion; it headed the asset tabulation of the top 100 industrial firms. A similar tabulation for 1966 revealed that the 100th listing in 1966 topped the 1917 levels except for U.S. Steel. Realizing that inflation blunts the conclusion, it still is apparent — perhaps now even a truism — that bigness is integral to our industrial makeup.

Assets cost money, and the ante keeps rising. Annual investments in plant and facilities may run into the hundreds of millions of dollars, with automation equipment contributing to these huge sums. Invariably, the next generation of automated machinery will be more expensive than the present one, and the spiral will undoubtedly continue. Inflation plays its part and the "black boxes" are not the same, rarely will the replacement be a 1:1 substitute for the predecessor. The point, in brief, is this: the threshold levels both for entry and sustenance have risen. The consequences: the number of new entrants is limited, the cost of a blunder may be fatal, and the game may be left to the sometimes questionable competition practiced by the oligopolistic giants. Pockets of a particular market may be free of these constraints, if the entrepreneur can sense a gap or unfulfilled need and find a profitable means of serving it. This avenue is still open:

> Foreign cars probably have a significant and permanent share in our domestic car market, and in the computer field, the only profitable computer firms, other than IBM, are those that successfully pierced IBM's flanks. These two examples illustrate typical modes of market entry. Foreign car penetration springboarded from established, well-to-do European companies. Their achievement created major policy shifts by the Big Three and the repercussions still persist. On the other hand, the successful non-IBM computer participants could not boast of any wealthy corporate support. They all brought the same credentials to their ventures: perception of a market opportunity, brains, financial backing, and no corporate base to offer a sheltering umbrella. Even with their success, the impact upon IBM has been minimal, with no discernible influence upon its share of the market. Where corporate giants have challenged IBM head-on, their losses to date have been huge, and tolerable only within the confines of a business entity that can generate the needed financial resources and still remain a viable economic institution even with

a gaping hole in its side. These stalwarts are few in number, and still fewer combine the capability and management daring to pursue such a precarious course.

From the economic standpoint, the risks of dominance by giants are several. Accepting the classic arguments depicting the ills of monopoly or oligopoly, let me turn to the high-technology-based industries — those industries where our growth has been the most rapid. Can they provide the continued momentum for economic advancement if the field only allows the giant player to compete? Without being dogmatic on the subject, I think not, and we have numerous examples to support this contention. At the very least, one expects that the large enterprise performs its present tasks well but is often inertia-ridden when it must mount substantial efforts in a new direction especially where the impetus derives from outside sources or pressures. If, indeed, technology change maintains a fast pace or even accelerates, can the giant move quickly enough to capitalize upon the change?

From the social standpoint, the literature offers much for the interested reader, and I will not tread over familiar ground. If the points suggested, however, are realistic and Big Business does tend to limit the number of participants at least in several industries, there is only one source of counterbalance: Big Government. I am not implying that the game is being played in underhanded fashion, in a manner similar to the machinations associated with the rise of several major industries in the late 1800's. The paramount need to be emphasized is that some mechanism should consistently offer the large industrial members alternatives that serve broader ends than just the economic betterment of the various participants. And this dialog or confrontation, as the case may be, should be continuous and meaningful rather than limited to the crisis situations or impotent measures that often typify an ineffectual compromise.

Perhaps the two considerations merge. If the economic drawbacks of Bigness can be nullified or at least muted, then the negative social implications will simultaneously diminish.

The business risks associated with the introduction of new automated systems will be intensified by the conflicting trends of changing technology vs. the social and economic needs of our society.

Economic Realities Predominate

The spectre of rapid-changing technology creating a stream of transformations in the automation process, with the interval between changes constantly being reduced, poses a perplexing problem for the automation user. The compression of an equipment's life cycle invariably forces the user to insure that its use is justified since the allowance for error is slight or nonexistent. At its admittedly ridiculous extreme, the business enterprise would allocate in zero time a large expense over a fixed output — exactly the opposite of automation's optimum environment. Yet technology's onrush pushes us toward that end, at least in asymptotic fashion. Automation flourishes best on a diet of infinite volume of a uniform product over an indefinite time period:

> The Model T experience perhaps serves as a unique paragon. Over an 18-year period Ford produced 15 million homogeneous units with the aid of his new mass-production techniques (and grossed $7 billion in that interval). Ironically, this very success sowed the seeds for the company's loss of market dominance and eventual near collapse during WW II. But in his day, Ford created — much to his credit — the automation ideal.

But the wonderful one-horse shay can also lead to disastrous calamity when fortune or management ineptitude does not generate the optimum conditions:

> In 1948, a British engineer designed what was billed as the first automatic radio factory. All the radio's electronic circuitry was assembled via machines with no human participation. The inventor claimed that 50 people and his machine could outproduce 1500 workers using traditional radio-construction methods. But, alas, when misfortune befell the customer for whom the machine was built to supply a huge volume of radios — Chiang's Nationalist China — the order was cancelled and the machine never was put to use.

As newer variations of the automation process appear, they may be applied in two modes: modernization of an existing facility or placement in a new plant. For the latter situation, the rationale for expansion via an enlarged capacity must be coupled with an anticipated increase in product demand. But when modernization is the underlying motivation, then we are dealing with a more complex circumstance: perhaps increased production or throughput is the impetus but more likely lower unit costs (by displacing human power at less expense) or the desire (need) for better quality prevails. Or the pressure can emanate from a competitor who has installed newer improved equipment. To complicate the timing factor, other considerations must be reviewed.

Referring to the Ford analogy, the Model T at its price offered a unique capability: Ford's innovation was the creation of a new market plus the organization to profitably service that market's demands. This type of newness persists today although the singularity generally is not the function itself but some variation of how it is achieved; the secret formula of Coke or Polaroid's instant film processing comes to mind. Greater affluence and increased discretionary income, however, not to mention the multiplicity of fads (tailfins on the car) or changing trends (the volatility in men's fashions), imply both lower volume of a given product and simply more products — both can be hostile factors to automation success. Two saving graces may be the rising population — more people — reinforced by greater purchasing power at the low end of the economic scale.

The potential for automation adversity presses in from two sides: technology forcing change, and a demand often inimical to allowing that change to pay off. The case cited for the automatic radio factory is, admittedly, extreme and improbable, but by no means impossible of repetition. The variations abound:

From 1964-1966, color TV receiver sales grew at over 80 percent per annum, compounded. In 1967 the outlook held similar promise and the industry geared up accordingly with automated equipments participating in the preparation. From 1966 to 1968, the growth rate dropped to 11 percent; the falloff resulted from the convergence of several adverse conditions. The industry reeled, and is probably still caught in the hangover of depressed expectations. All participants have suffered to some degree, although most depend on multi-product lines and the exact price of the miscalculation is buried in corporate data.

It is axiomatic that the only information available to the decision-maker describes past occurrences, and the accuracy of such inputs is often subject to question. Yet if there is one thing we know with absolute certainty it is the inevitable wrongness of past trends projected into tomorrow's activity. Like it or not, technology change, via automation or other means, forces us to discredit the past and grapple with the much more elusive future. The only contradiction of that thesis suggests that we "turn off" technology or impose a moratorium on technological advancement. This attitude harks back 150 years when the Industrial Revolution was picking up momentum; it is a modern-day Luddite philosophy and is as untenable and irrational now as it was then. I believe (hope?) that an artificial technology slowdown will not be enacted (by whatever means), but it is reasonable to expect that technology's cause can best be served if technology's offshoots can be better anticipated and planned for.

Relevant Keys to Success

In part, better planning involves more information – more timely and more accurate. But those who view today's high-speed data-processing system as the panacea may find that the proposed solution actually contributes to the problem. For information gathering requires a prior decision: Which information should be gathered? This then leads to "what is needed?" which finally brings us to the end of the road: why is the information being collected in the first place? Now the problem is really confronted and the computer's benefits are placed in their proper perspective, namely, that the initial onus lies squarely on management's shoulders. No matter how fast or how much information can be obtained, little is gained unless the human element has clearly asked the relevant questions and then forced the data-gathering system to slavishly respond to these needs.

This is not a simple task. It requires a special kind of person (whom I will describe more fully in the succeeding section). His job is not made easier by the environment in which he must perform. As mentioned previously, the demands of a pluralistic society, both industrial and consumer, frustrate any simplistic projection of past trends, especially for long-term forecasts. The reasons:

1. Product availability abounds as new products appear and older ones are retained or dropped, thereby proliferating the choice alternatives open to the user.

2. Demographic shifts, most of which are predictable, modify existing demand patterns even if product variation is zero.

3. Social changes, most of which are unpredictable, revamp social values and mores, thereby introducing discontinuities — sometimes extreme — in traditional or even changing product demands or availability.

4. The influence of governmental actions, often unpredictable and unexpected, generates change by fiat.

5. The awareness and subsequent responses to world events may induce responses of short or long duration.

Change has always been incurred by movements in each of these areas. It is the rapidity and often the depth of today's change that add a dimension of challenge to our insight into the future:

No less than 150 years ago, communication was practiced as it had been for centuries before. In 1832 Morse's telegraph and in 1876 Bell's telephone allowed instant communication over wires. Marconi disposed of the wires about the turn of the century, and television later added a picture. Now the prospects appear more likely that we will utilize existing technology in new ways rather than seeking new forms. The communications satellite, the marriage between computers and communication media, and the laser innovation might alter our means of information sensing and gathering in the next 30 years as much as the notable inventions cited did in the past 130 years.

The disruption of existing patterns is inevitable. The problems — and the opportunities — will set exacting demands for business management.

As automation penetrates more deeply into the world's industrial environment, management's greatest challenge lies in its utilization of our greatest asset — the skilled knowledge worker.

If automation is carried to its ultimate conclusion, we might envision production lines without people, infinitely sensitive to output variations, and with self-imposed controls to monitor quality and other characteristics. Accepting that this end may never be achieved — for many possible reasons — it still represents a model directing the automation effort. If this end is reached, it imposes constant pressures upon other segments of the business organization, e.g., marketing, procurement, warehousing and distribution, and, of course, the management role. If better means of automation are not matched by the capability to integrate automation's output with the other organisms of the business, then the operation is not functioning at peak efficiency and automation advances may have passed the point of diminishing returns. In short, industrial automation seeks the optimization of one segment of the business; as it approaches this goal, the spotlight moves to other functions.

These are numerous examples of companies thriving via their superb performance in one phase of the business operation: the company that consistently outpaces the competition by its capability in generating a steady stream of new products ahead of the field, or by its skill at manufacturing a high-volume item regardless the point of origination, or by its finesse at convincing the market place of its products' attributes. In the long run, the consistently prosperous firm does many things well or at least it does few things poorly (and nothing important very poorly).

Inevitably the large investment in automation and the success in its implementation dictate that management recognize and excel in the integration of the various functions performed within the organization. This is a difficult chore and only recently have we seen two of industry's giants resort to committee management at the very top. Most good managers are strong in one area and adequate in many others. Often the characteristics conducive to the development of a particular skill are at variance with the attributes required in ancillary fields. It is not uncommon in the engineering arena to reward technical expertise with managerial status and, probably more often than not, the good engineer becomes the inept manager. Only infrequently have I encountered an engineering manager who can do both well — and for good reason.

In the art of venture capital investment, the investing party is often naive concerning even the important features of a company's product (product line). And, the investor maintains, that it is not important that he have this information. He looks for assets in a company's management that argue for success: the ability to view the whole rather than just a part, the sensitivity to his customers' needs rather than an obsession with the details of how these needs can be fulfilled, the conception of how the parts must blend and grow together.

Although a top management should possess the broader insights needed to sharpen the whole organization, invariably it must delegate major responsibility to a subordinate group. And the members of this group must also command a multifaceted viewpoint. Some will specialize, while others will be more general in their outlook. What kind of people will they be? Their background probably embraces these features: they are well-educated, well-paid, possessed of broad interests, stimulated only within bounds by pecuniary motivation, and sensitive to many social and secular issues. Their skills are in demand and so they are mobile and sometimes even rootless. How does a management attract such persons and, having obtained them, how does it keep them happy, creative, and stationary? Many of the perquisites won't work, nor will the stock-option plan, yearly bonus, or executive privileges be the answer. In short, I suggest that successful inroads by automation will compel business management to seek and find a "troublesome" breed of worker. This worker will demand a different treatment and environment, the absence of which may compromise the benefits reaped from automation originally.

Although this skilled knowledge worker will exert a different set of pressures upon business management, the automation vis-a-vis worker dialog generally follows a different path. The overwhelming mass of literature on this subject considers worker displacement, new skill requirements, social implications, and the like. There is a major significant factor which is often overlooked and which, I believe, may be more fundamental to automation's role.

Industrial automation for the foreseeable future will include some manual labor contribution. The total "automation-no humans" setting is usually quite expensive and whether it is a desirable goal to shoot for is questionable — except in rare circumstances. Where the man/machine combination offers the optimum resultant, what characteristics typify the human's contribution? — generally, low skill levels, limited education, little or no initiative or creativity, and minimum wage requirements. In the high-volume production assembly processes, where automation is most conspicuous and best justified, the dependence upon a human resource with the parameters described implies a contradiction for U.S. industry. This is not an asset for which U.S. labor can offer any leverage; quite the contrary, numerous countries possess amply comparative economic advantage since they can offer lower wages. Ironically, not only does this dependence represent a trending toward a relative weakness, it moves us away from a relative strength. And that strength we excel in — the knowledge, skills, and expertise which the world's finest educational system provides to a broad spectrum of America's population. I can best illustrate this dichotomy with an example from my own background:

> Electronics, and most typically semiconductor electronic components, pass through three stages of development in the sequence from idea genesis to mass production. The three stages, in turn, are brains-intensive, capital-intensive, and labor-intensive. At the outset, the ingenuity of one man or a group conceives of a new product or process and performs the first steps toward translating idea into reality (brains-intensive). Then the infant product advances to a prototype production line and the inevitable "debugging" minimizes the problems inherent in the production process actually fabricating the core of the electronic component, e.g., a silicon chip for a transistor or integrated circuit (capital-intensive). Finally, as learning curve improvements raise the overall production efficiency, the automation contribution approximates a constant/volume factor, which naturally approaches zero with sufficient output. And then the labor contribution predominates, a factor largely independent of volume. The movement to low-cost labor areas — originally Japan, but now Taiwan, Hong Kong, South Korea, and Singapore — testifies to the credibility of the original thesis (labor-intensive).

At present, the electronics industry is split on the free trade issue: the component makers seek protectionism in some form while the high-volume equipment makers generally favor free trade without constraints (since many of their products are also assembled overseas). When labor becomes the cost-reduction limitation and when the volume level justifies the action, the labor-intensive activity moves outside the U.S. The emotion-packed free trade issue pivots on this labor ingredient; where protectionism is advocated the argument usually is based on the lower labor costs in other countries and our inability to compete. Haven't our labor rates always been high, relative and absolute?

The long-term implications are clear. The movement of technology and automation advances between countries is accelerating. And we do not have a monopoly on the brains needed for innovation. It is highly unlikely that our labor force will ever be less costly than those in numerous other countries. These realities present a challenging scenario for business management. If most practical automation does require a blue-collar input, can we achieve a continuing technology advantage to counteract our labor disadvantage?

Two aspects of the automation/worker question have been aired. They pose fundamental uncertainties for the long-term viability of automation in several important applications. They even may be deserving of a rethinking on the optimum role of automation in our industrial society.

Conclusions

A century ago, automation was unborn and mechanization was still a fledgling. The underlying impetus favoring the movement to automation has not changed and, with the vast increase in the world's population, its argument is stronger than ever. We need more automation offering man a greater opportunity to do what only the human can do or what he can do better than a machine. The fallout of social problems and criticism asserts that automation is under scrutiny, and the business/economic community must therefore examine its own position. The regression of technology and automation is not the answer, while an indifference to the questions is even worse. Ultimately, the users of the automation instrument should examine this powerful tool within the context of its economic and social consequences. Either considered without the other is inadequate.

APPENDIX

The few specific issues chosen to be discussed do not reflect our priorities on this subject. We have opted for depth rather than breadth and have therefore selected material both relevant and familiar to our experience. Other issues related to the general area of this discussion include:

1. Social costs incurred to increase productivity.
2. Depletion and defacement of natural resources.
3. The inadequacy of social institutions to regulate the distribution of productivity's outputs.
4. The disruptive influence on employment patterns and subsequent social malaise.
5. Mechanisms to regulate the flow of technology into useful channels.
6. The relationship between the technologist and his social environment.
7. The inexactness with which technology advances can be forecast and their consequences determined.
8. The role of automation as a macroeconomic factor.
9. Automation's contribution to bridging the gap between the "haves" and "have nots."
10. Automation's impact on the productivity of capital.

11

Questions of Size, Affluence, and Displacement

Chairman:
Howard R. Smith

Deliberations on the Economic Aspects of Automation

Howard R. Smith, Head, Department of Management, University of Georgia, holds a BA, Simpson College; MA and Ph.D, Louisiana State University. He has studied at University of Iowa, Stanford University and Harvard Graduate School of Business Administration. Dr. Smith is director of the Executive Development Program at the University of Georgia, and is a consultant to government and business. Books he has written include *Economic History of the United States* and *Democracy and Public Interest.*

An important preface to a summary of these discussions is the proposition that fundamental agreement is virtually non-existant in any significant area of the economic scene. And a large element in this is the absence of hard data in this entire field. Nevertheless, effective reaching toward consensus can be done — a better understanding of the basic universal forces involved being one of the objectives of this symposium.

A related but much broader prefatory proposition is that it is very difficult to pin down dependable causal relationships between automation and economic/business variables. There are several reasons for this. The most immediately evident is the fact that this is a complex, dynamic society, in which the concurrent operation of numerous factors makes doubtful the validity of isolating even one for intellectual examination. Second, when automation is defined with some vigor — as meaning something more specific than a continuation of the rapid technological change which has characterized this country's economy for many decades — there is perhaps a lot less automation around than is often supposed.

Put differently, because of a wide variety of "frictions" of the sort that accompany any evolution, we are becoming an automated society less rapidly than much contemporary journalism suggests. Finally, in a number of ways there is evidenced around us a tendency to attribute to (blame) automation much more than can honestly be laid to its door.

Is Size a Problem?

Nevertheless, there is no doubt that automation does add some extra push to what is happening. Thus there is stemming from this source an additional dynamism, and extra accentuation of some trends which would otherwise have less force.

For example, Dr. Kleiman's proposition that, "Automation will be instrumental in accelerating the dominance by a breed of business giants possessing increasing influence and control over our economic destinies," raises significant question. There are those who doubt that this really will be a consequence of automation — who pointedly suggest the absence of dependable data for reference, and who also call attention to some of the ways in which automation is developing that do *not* provide sole advantage to bigness. There are even those who are quite confident that public (antitrust) policy will in any case prevent automation's growth from contributing significantly to giantism.

By and large it is the large companies that can afford to emphasize enterprise instead of company. For example, the computer operation of one large company is generally conceded to have been very unprofitable during the past decade or so. But, this will probably become a most successful operation, not because of its own capability, but because it has a protective umbrella over it and all the time it has been able to draw upon the resources of an enterprise with the ability to tolerate the losses because of other very profitable operations. A major difficulty lies with the one-product young firm. Usually, the business risk here is much greater and the only money that comes into such enterprises is the capital money willing to take the big risks of loss in order to incur the big returns as well as problems.

Many of our smaller companies today are surviving well because the larger companies are not out doing their field work. There are many major businesses in this country that have not had the courage to face up to the realities and make some needed changes; but there are other major companies that are trying desperately to change the business they are in. They are companies of the past ten or twenty years that were once considered as the Rock of Gibralter. However, it does not appear that size alone makes the feeling in the executive suite any easier, particularly with the fast pace of technology. Large corporations can die and we are going to see some big ones die in our lifetime. It seems that the small, viable companies have an advantage in the mere fact that they are viable, more flexible.

What Way to Move?

However, given some probabilities here — that bigness favors technological intensification by way of automation, and that automation in turn favors the further growth of the giants — what are the implications? It is widely supposed that one of the consequences would be an intensification of problems of external/social diseconomies of which we have of late become so conscious — and not least because of the sheer diseconomies arising from a speeding up of the process of socioeconomic change. One of the prime ways in which these diseconomies must be redressed is action by government. But, the issue of how much and what kind of government action is desirable, understandably, depends greatly how large are the "sins" we attribute to automation. More specifically, it matters what view we take toward the worker displacement that is attributable to automation progress. If there is here a mass phenomenon, where the remedy would seem to rest on significant institutional intervention, government would have to be asked to assist in the making of large structural adjustments. On the other hand, if the correct image is rather of a succession of individual adjustments to the changing scene, the government could well content itself with "guaranteeing" enough assistance to minimize unemployment friction.

Dr. Kleiman has suggested a trend, something that might very well happen, given certain circumstances. However, you have the pressure of technology, the creation of new and different things which offer something better, quicker, easier, etc. On the other hand, you have society, which really isn't awfully sensitive to technology per se, but it is in a certain state of flux itself due to many conditions — it could be from government activity; it could be from social changes which we are all familiar with; it could be from career influence. The aspirations of society on the one hand and the results of technology on the other may actually be opposites. Today, the trend is moving toward giving society what it wants rather than it being a collision course between the two.

In the early years of automation, engineering effort was directed mainly toward finding great uniformity of product, but of necessity today applications to meet the demand for product flexibility are growing. The manufacturer must maintain flexibility if he is going to survive. There is no doubt that concepts offering flexibility in automation are expanding.

The higher flexibility automation, thus, is just entering the manufacturing process. Ten years from now the systems installed in response to flexibility of market demand will be pretty sophisticated systems and, economically speaking, pretty significant equipment.

From the overall standpoint, a good example is found in the electronics area: The major innovation in electronics is the integrated circuit — the successor to the transistor. It has been known for approximately ten years, but has been in production for only about five years. It has had an impact on the industrial scene and on military equipment but it hasn't as yet reached consumer goods. One of the reasons here is there is a great deal of volatility not only in knowledge but in nature of demand for the end product. The technology has been changing rapidly in this area — demand has gone up, volume has gone up tremendously, and this generally argues for some movement toward automation. The technology is pushing one way and the nature of the demand for the product is pushing another way. The importance of getting an integrated circuit into a television set is moot.

The Risks are High

A most critical factor that must be recognized is the risk of the application of old technology to automate manufacture versus the fear of new technology — how new technology will change major requirements. The economic "unknown" factor is often the write-off time available for achieving economic automation. In addition, the reduction of cost is to a great extent the function of product design. In doing studies of unit costs, you find very quickly that the limitation may often be that the product design is not very amenable to automation, although it can be done. Another limitation is the economic problem of building sophisticated automated equipment that can handle a complex product, and then suddenly learning that that equipment will not be usable because of changed configuration demanded by the product designers.

With regard to changes inhibiting automation, it would appear there are two different kinds — one is created by consumer demand and the other by manufacturers. When you get to the point where a technique or a methodology is involved primarily for the sake of change or when there are changes that do not have anything to do with the essential function of the product, you find automation inhibited severely.

We must make the assumption that we are going to continue to automate and we *are* going to have to automate if we
are to compete in a world market. How are we to compete
unless we design systems which ultimately use less labor than
the other fellow? Or, to put it in other economic terms, that
increase our productivity.

Technology is becoming more mobile. Also, it seems that
the present cost differential in the labor forces is probably
going to be more or less permanent. Why should we expect
that we in the long run are not going to have to work as hard
as the next fellow if we are going to keep ahead of him? The
Japanese have essentially been copying a great deal of the
technology from the United States since the war, and they
have copied it very well. Obviously, they are going to be a
force to be reckoned with if they move ahead.

Changes in Approach Needed

There are two very basic factors that we have to consider
and perhaps be worried about. One bears on the education
area, and the other one is an economic problem particularly
related to this discussion. It appears that the rate at which we
introduce technology into our society — certainly this
encompasses automation — is dependent on two factors,
more than anything else. One is the rate at which we train
people in levels of thinking which some of our people have
and many of our people can't even imagine exists. I think our
future society will hinge upon total changes in our whole
educational process.

The other aspect is a financial one, because the application
of technology and certainly of automation is dependent upon
a considerable investment ahead of the time in order to raise
the productivity of our system. Yet, we face something in
this country now which should worry all of us — our balance

of payments problem which is having an increasing dampening effect on our domestic economy.

The only significant attack that can be made to redress this imbalance is through further increases of our productivity and thus our competitive position. And yet one of our responses to that problem and other domestic problems is the action we have taken through our financial medium to tighten up credit and make credit more expensive. And it is the fluidity of the financial medium which is, along with education, the controller and significant agent in the rate or pace at which we can automate. By doing the things we are doing in our country now in this financial effort, we are working against ourselves. We are working to use an imperfect tool with long lag which tends to, not so much by the cost of money but by the uncertainty it introduces, slow down the very industrial process of adding automation at the time this country desperately needs to add automation.

Some of the economic discussion concerning automation and society seems to be ideological/historical at the root. Against the strong claim that a society which has been highly fragmented in its approach to all kinds of issues must now more vigorously plan for contingencies before they arise, the emphatic observation is made that somehow but regrettably this society has already become too tightly knit. Only part relates directly to the automation issue as such. However, some of those who see a necessity for broadly expanding the role of a "big brother" government express fear that such a government, augmented by today's and foreseeable information technology, could easily be a very high price to pay for such questionable "help."

Partly for these reasons, government is not seen as the only or key avenue of redress against the build-up of social/economic diseconomies. Another important counterforce will be business social responsibility attitudes and behaviors. To be sure, not everyone agrees on why businessmen exhibit these attitudes and behaviors. Moreover, it is fully understood that automation does not in any sense stand as a sole, and not necessarily even a large, causal factor behind this phenomenon. But few doubt that we are today witnessing a significantly different business community from this standpoint, that this is a trend which can only become more manifest, and that it will help reduce the need for any rapid growth of government responsibilities.

The Labor Scene

Discussions have been voluminous concerning various aspects of the labor force in an automating society. There seems to be a rather wide consensus on the proposition that the mix of skills/talent required will steadily move toward the high capacity/large responsibility end of this spectrum. This of course has become "conventional wisdom."

When industry invests in a million-dollar piece of machinery that is to run around the clock, seven days a week, the demand is for a pretty intelligent attendant, not necessarily a college trained person — a person who is an experienced operator or a mechanic and who now has developed a great many additional judgments/skills capabilities. In fact, one of the exciting things experienced is the natural human jump at the opportunity to have a higher skilled job which uses more judgment. The very value of the equipment put on the line dictates the kind of people and the more productivity obtained. Systems have been put on the line that have increased productivity as much as 10 to 1, and when a company takes this type of step, every minute is a very expensive proposition. The person at the bottom of the whole line of command, who is going to stay with that equipment day and night, has got to have a considerable amount of good judgment. That is what makes their job "fun" compared to the monotonous, simple duty they were performing before — they are called on to use some pretty exciting judgment, because the machinery is *not* without its problems.

However, there may be an added twist here which significantly parts company with what "everybody knows." This assertion is that in automated industry as we now know it and will experience it in the foreseeable future, the irreducible minimum of blue-collar labor cost would perhaps not add much to the balance-of-payments inhibition in foreign trade that we are also up against.

Inevitably, discussion about the labor force turns to the displacement of men by machines. And here, too, there is substantial agreement that one of the fads of the day is greatly to overdramatize the rate at which this displacement is taking place — particularly by the use of gross figures rather than net as well as by ignoring ordinary everyday changes. Even more specifically, the process through which men are displaced by automation is rather less direct than is often supposed.

At the micro level, for example, the automating firm is likely to be an expanding one — with the result that more employees are shortly needed rather than less. Moreover, as a consequence of the lead-time planning which is more and more characteristic of such concerns, people are reshuffled internally or moved so directly to satisfactory employment elsewhere that minimum adjustment discomfort ensues. Which is to say that the displacement problem will most likely originate in those sectors of the economy — firms or industry — which are *not* vigorous enough to maintain themselves intact.

In macro terms this means that the labor displacement process in an automating society follows essentially the same dynamics as in earlier technological advance. Thus economic sectors not keeping pace with the rest of the economy lose resources — some of these being released workers who do not readily find alternative or acceptable opportunities. In this way there is created a sort of a "pool" of the technologically unemployed, and the measures of the magnitude of this problem are rate of input into the pool and the effectiveness of the work of keeping these people satisfactorily employable in the new technology context. And of course the causal role of automation here is the speed of its introduction and therefore the education/training task its needs impose upon use.

Here, necessarily, some of this reshaping of the labor force can be achieved by collaboration with available education facilities. Education policy outside but adjacent to the business sector must accept *much* of this responsibility — both by working directly with those already in the unemployment pool, and by more effective development assistance for the pre-labor force group.

In the words of one observer, "Our engineers say we get so smart so late and we don't always have the ultimate idea at the beginning, but we do simplify things and make it easier to operate these complex systems. Computer programmers are certainly much more sophisticated now than any workers were in Charles Dickens' time or even thirty years ago. I think we will find our people on continually higher plateaus, even though in any given decade their particular job may be made easier for them when man's mind is applied properly. Actually, all the areas we are talking about today will be academic when our children have reached our age — they'll be worrying about all kinds of new problems. There is after all literally no end to new levels of sophistication."

12

Re-education
for an Age of Automation

Roger W. Bolz

Roger W. Bolz, President, Automation for Industry, Inc., is a registered professional engineer and received his engineering education at Case Institute of Technology. Following engineering service in a variety of industries, Mr. Bolz spent 24 years in technical editing and publishing and was editor-in-chief of *Automation* magazine before becoming a full-time consultant on automation planning and application. His most recent writing is the book *Understanding Automation — Elements for Managers*. He is widely known in the field of product design engineering for his earlier text, *Production Processes — The Producibility Handbook*. Mr. Bolz was recently honored with election to Fellow member of the American Society of Mechanical Engineers for outstanding contributions to the profession.

The future starts now. Most assuredly, if we examine carefully, the character of this future is mirrored in the events of the past.

Today's decisions, based largely on past performance and achievement, will relentlessly shape the future. Seldom will it be done through massive long-range edicts but mostly through a long series of short-range steps continuously redirected and aimed toward the desired goal.

If the events of the past are misread by intent or accident important decisions for shaping the future can be calamitous. This Symposium has as its fundamental purpose to examine the place of automation as the salient factor in the production of goods and services, and to understand how it affects and is affected by all other aspects of the economy.

History Speaks

Like the far-sighted prognosticator of 1897 who saw all farmland being gobbled up in 20 years to provide oats for the rapidly rising horse population, we too can easily look at the wrong indicators. To see the future most realistically requires that we see the automobile that was on the scene in 1897 despite the impact of the horse population. And even though the total number of horses did indeed increase, they were used more and more for pleasure, not power, and automation of the farm solved the feed problem.

Dr. Earl L. Butz, Dean of Continuing Education, Purdue University, objects vehemently to the apologetic attitude of many engineers, scientists and economists with regard to automation, "Don't apologize," he correctly points out, "The advantages far outweigh any possible undesired effects. Ignorance and misinformation created by fiction writers have conspired to create a great myth. The great myth is that automation fosters loss of employment and is in fact antisocial in character. The truth is precisely the opposite.

In our advanced economy with its proliferating markets and products, recourse to automation techniques is often the only practical answer to the need for low-priced products, mass market satisfaction, high quality and precision where labor is demanding and expensive.

Automation is merely a part of the vast technology of our industrial and scientific complex. Its principles are based on almost a hundred and eighty years of engineering research and development that began with the fundamental concept for an automatic flour mill invented by Oliver Evans in 1783.

What is it? Nothing more or less than the technology of manufacturing, processing or performing services as automatically and continuously as business economics demand.

The *key* is economics. The *stimuli* are competition and consumer demand.

First, let's recognize that automation is with us. Its use in manufacturing has been expanding gradually over the years. We are obliged to recognize its help and its major contribution to our standard of living. One need only look at the shelves in the local hardware or grocer's to see the typical output of automated operations and plants.

Properly applied, it makes possible desired goods and services at reasonable prices through two advantages: greater productivity, without added labor, and increased throughput. In 1920 a telephone call from New York to San Francisco cost $20 and for the same price 1037 letters could be sent. Today the same call costs $2.85 but only 47 letters can be sent for the same price!

Early in the 1800's it is recorded* that a member of the French Assembly introduced a bill specifying that all wood cutting shall be done only with a dull ax, ostensibly to insure work. With typical French humor the bill stated that any sharpening would be considered an offense against public policy!

It seems that problems of consumer demand, job availability, production efficiency and related areas of economic life have changed but little over the years. Now, in place of the cry, "Machines have taken your place," that appeared following the Civil War, the new theme is "automation."

In reality, the focus today is on a problem that is far reaching in its significance. It calls for a new penetrating look at the economic structure, and a renewed interest in our free enterprise heritage and the individual's good. There is no easy answer. Understanding holds the only enduring promise.

Economic Pressures

Few investigations to date have bothered to deal with the fundamental realism of industrial enterprise and evolutionary change. Industry was born of service. It has developed by serving the material needs of the individual and not merely by providing jobs. The entrepreneur makes a job for himself and others by developing a service or product that attracts customers. American freedom and free enterprise created the conditions under which all are free to take advantage of the opportunity to make themselves or the product of their skills and thinking valuable to others, even indispensable.

Economic Sophisms by Frederic Bastiat, D. Van Nostrand Co., Inc., Princeton, N.J., 1964.

Certainly the history of industrial growth has not been one of machines creating problems. Consumer demand and its influence on business outlook has in large part been the troublemaker. Industrial development is relatively slow and unsteady. By and large, it follows from the stimulus of consumer demand. As the consumer's attitude, actions, and outlook swing in wide variations, industrial effort to serve follows suit with tremendous backwash effect on the fortunes of all workmen involved throughout a great interwoven maze of connected services. The consumer and jobholder for the most part is the victim of his own choices and whims.

Looking at the facts, the simple truth about all machinery is that it works for everyone. The automobile, the washing machine, the gas furnace, the refrigerator, all serve to conserve effort and make life . more enjoyable. As such, all machinery obviously eliminates the need to do some kinds of work, of course. Witness the blacksmith, the glass blower, the tinker and even the housewife — but the result has been a continuing stream of new kinds of work — in operating the equipment, servicing it, helping design and build it, and selling its product, as well as in utterly new industries and services. Outmoded occupations decline — recruitment and opportunity emerge in new fields. The common denominator is change. Today, Symposium participants have observed, 60 per cent of active jobs fall into services and that during the past decade the big job growth has been in services — some 17 million new ones — equalling the total employment in the manufacturing area.

Because of change, one of the growing problems of recent years in relation to automation has been in communications — communicating an understanding of what's happening and why. Most important is the fact that economic survival of the United States in the years ahead will require more and better automation. To gain the widely implied affluence so often discussed will demand better understanding by every citizen, continuing research and development, and intensified study of the automation technology by engineers.

The way people look at automation is highly colored by their own ideas and by their personal experiences. Ask the man who sits in an air conditioned cab and operates a rolling mill how he likes that machine and he will tell you in glowing terms how it beats the old days when he bent, perspiring at the hot rolls. But ask him what he thinks of automation, and he is apt to launch into a diatribe about how it is "throwing people out of work."

Our technology is changing, of course, and this often brings about short-term dislocations and displacements of workers. But this has been going on for a long time and invariably leads to the upgrading of those workers into jobs of higher skills at higher pay. A familiar example is the rapidly vanishing ice-man, who used to deliver ice to old-fashioned iceboxes which opened at the top and dripped water at the bottom. The mechanical refrigerator changed all that under the approving smiles of the housewife. For every single ice-man of old, you will find hundreds today who are manufacturing refrigerators, repairing them or selling them in air-conditioned stores — all jobs which pay a great deal more and require considerably less manual effort, and which never existed in the days of the icebox.

Effects of Change

The pervasive myth that effects of automation in some manner must be "cushioned," sidesteps the issue of just how do we obtain all the goods and services desired? Fulfilling the demand for goods, meeting the need for reasonable prices, maintaining a rising wage scale, reducing the hours worked, and creating better working conditions make automation an imperative.

The main problems that face both management and labor in this regard are far different than have been ordinarily presented. On one hand, ill-timed pressures by labor and government can and do put an actual end to the business with total loss of jobs. The newspaper businesses of New York are clearly one of the multitude of these problems. Urban renewal is another. Automation is also clearly not the problem here for there is none. The mythmakers have effectively established the idea that machines put people "out of work." On the contrary, increasing use of machines is being forced through such means as minimum wage laws, wage increases without matching rises in productivity, and rising taxes.

Seldom does one hear anything about the cost and effort required to combat these adverse conditions. Automation is no automatic answer. It must be recognized here that entering into the increasingly complex areas of automation technology is costly and hazardous.* It is vital that the industry has an attitude of real support and dedication to productivity advance. Genuine understanding must exist in management circles. No one can assure success with automation other than the manufacturer himself and he must be ready to risk some funds or there will be no real advance. Unless there is motivation to invest there will be no automation and a laggard management can be caught unawares.

To introduce change, such as automation brings, requires strong motivation or some intensive driving force. Automation is no driving force; it is an evolving engineering technology. Research and development is the real driving force of change today. Various agencies of government have financed with tax money over two-thirds of the more than $100

---

*However, it is interesting to note it is *more* hazardous to avoid risk. Of the top 500 companies of 1900, only 70 are still on the scene. Of the top 100 of 1917, only 43 are among the top 100 today and 28 have disappeared entirely. Of the 200 fastest growing companies of 1940, only 30 are still in existence.

billion spent on R&D in the last decade. The "Manpower Report of the President," March, 1964, comments in this regard, "In view of the great expansion in R&D activities, it may seem surprising that productivity and technological change have not proceeded at an even faster pace. . ."

The "Report of the Committee on Utilization of Scientific and Engineering Manpower" by the National Academy of Sciences states, ". . . statistics alone do not fully reveal . . . the government's deep involvement in science and technology, creating a complex relationship involving the government, the universities, and private industry."

Thus, when the onus is placed on industry through oblique references to automation as the creator of change, nothing could be further from the truth. A careful look at various areas of change and their basic causes reveals that economics, government, and consumers will in fact "shape the future."

Future Aspects

Automation has been much maligned, sometimes revered, and frequently misunderstood. The things we read and hear about automation range from the wonderful to the ridiculous — from the proved fact to the wild rumor. Just how do we sift fact from fable?

The growing body of literature on automation and problems supposedly allied with it has been put forward mostly by social scientists, but it is industry that gets clobbered by misunderstanding and misconception. This Symposium on Automation and Society has been convened in order to help develop a better understanding of automation.

To orient our thinking about automation, we need to examine a few basic facts. First of all, industrial productivity in this country, as borne out by statistics, has increased for a century or more — and is still increasing. This tells us two things: 1. We could not have accomplished this at all without automation, and 2. Some degree of automation has been with us for a long time.

Up to now, American industry has a splendid record for meeting all demands put upon it in peace and war. But what comes next? Forecasts for 1985 — just 16 years from now — indicate that our labor force will reach 110 million, and our Gross National Product will zoom to $1.4 trillion. Here again, we notice that with a labor force increasing less than 50 per cent, we will have a GNP more than double. Will American industry prove equal to the task of meeting such needs?

These facts are clear: We began our "Industrial Revolution" more than two centuries ago by replacing human and animal energy with mechanical energy. We have been engaged for some time in an extension of that industrial revolution which might be summed up by the word "automation."

A Challenge

Automation, like technology, is a practical tool. Used with understanding it can provide major assistance in advancing our economic position. The challenge to us all is real and demanding. It is important to know and understand the general underlying facts of today's technology. Recognize that progress is never painless or automatic. Understand the economics of our competitive marketplace. Relatively lower cost products and services, with improved quality, are possible through automation, and the result will be increased availability of goods, increased employment, and greater enjoyment.

Our conclusion is we can be effective in meeting the needs of a changing economy.

In technology we will have to improve our knowledge of

how processing systems function; In sociological areas we will need imagination in dealing with critical problems of change; In our pursuit of education we must develop flexibility to adjust to new needs; In the area of economics we must develop better planning in depth to enable management to maintain a stable economic position with automation.

If American industry can continue to produce larger volumes of better products at lower costs with less manual labor, the horizons ahead will be brighter and better than any we have ever reached.

Appendix

Center for Study of Automation and Society

Information gained while planning the first annual Symposium on Automation and Society, and at the symposium itself emphasized two points.

First, there is a large requirement for information and service dealing with the automation-society relationship. Second, there is no central source for such information and service. A number of institutions have pursued various facets of the relationship. None, however, has approached it with the breadth attempted by the first Symposium on Automation and Society.

Encouraged by the success of the Symposium its co-sponsors set to work on plans for a more ambitious undertaking.

Result of these plans is the Center for the Study of Automation and Society. It was established as a non-profit corporation in Athens, Georgia, in the summer of 1969.

Purpose of the Center is "the continuing study of relationships between automation and society so as to encourage the development of automation in harmony with and for the benefit of society."

Co-sponsors of the Symposium — the University of Georgia and Reliance Electric Company, a producer of equipment and systems for automation — are the initial sponsors of the Center. The Center is undertaking projects in four principal areas:

- A data base to provide comprehensive and current information on completed and in-process work and statistics dealing with the automation-society relationship. A library, computer-based retrieval system and bibliographic publications are among the projects planned in this area.

- Research to generate ideas and information on the automation-society relationship from such standpoints as curriculum development, economic measurements, technological forecasting, labor and management policies, and planning for change. In addition to its own research the Center will provide study facilities for research projects initiated by others.

- Information, generated by research, annual symposia and other means, made public through monographs policy papers, periodicals, and audio-visual teaching materials.

- Consulting to those planning for automation in both technological and social terms.

Projects in these areas will involve both the Center personnel and the professional resources of a number of universities, corporations and agencies with which relationships are maintained. Work will be undertaken in the U.S. and abroad because the Center's interest, like the components of its study, is international.

The 1969 Georgia-Reliance Symposium
on Automation and Society

Symposium Committee

Ellis L. Scott, Chairman, Professor of Management, College of Business Administration and the Graduate School of Business, University of Georgia, Athens, Ga.

James W. Landers, Director of Public Relations, Reliance Electric Company, Cleveland, O.

Charles I. Yoder, President, Charles Yoder & Co., Cleveland, O.

Homer C. Cooper, Director of the Social Science Research Institute, University of Georgia, Athens, Ga.

Clarence C. Miley, Instructor, School of Business, University of Georgia, Athens, Ga.

Thomas W. Mahler, Director, Georgia Center for Continuing Education, University of Georgia, Athens, Ga.

Mario J. Goglia, Vice Chancellor for Research, University System of Georgia, Atlanta, Ga.

Howard R. Smith, Chairman, Dept. of Management and Director of the Executive Development Program, University of Georgia, Athens, Ga.

Roger W. Bolz, Consultant, Automation for Industry, Inc., Cleveland, O.

Symposium Co-Sponsors

The University of Georgia, Athens.
Graduate School of Business Administration
Social Science Research Institute
Georgia Center for Continuing Education
The Reliance Electric Co., Cleveland, O.

Participants

Burton W. Adkinson, Head of the Office of Science Information Service, National Science Foundation, Washington.

Hiram Barksdale, College of Business Administration, University of Georgia.

Calvin L. Beale, Economic Research Service, Department of Agriculture.

John A. Bekker, Director, Market Information Services, AVM Corp., Jamestown, N.Y.

William S. Bradford, Commissioner, Federal Mediation and Concilliation Service, Atlanta.

Thomas W. Butler, Jr., Director, Cooley Electronics Laboratory, University of Michigan.

Earl L. Butz, Dean of Continuing Education, Purdue University.

Ralph R. Canter, Military Manpower Research Coordinator, Office of the Secretary of Defense.

C. Ray Carpenter, Research Professor, Psychology and Anthropology, University of Georgia.

L.J. Carr, Vice President-Marketing, Industrial Drives Group, Reliance Electric Company.

Gordon B. Carson, Vice President for Business and Finance, Ohio State University.

Melvyn R. Copen, Associate Professor, Production & Logistics Management, and Director of Graduate Studies, College of Business Administration, University of Houston.

Thomas R. Corn, Manager, Marketing Research and Planning, Reliance Electric Company, Cleveland, O.

Morris Dantzker, Manager of Computer Technology and Technical Director, Auerbach Institute, Philadelphia.

Ralph G. Davis, Vice President-Operations, Reliance Electric Company, Cleveland, O.

Robert C. Davis, Associate Professor of Sociology, Division of Special Interdisciplinary Studies, Case Western Reverve University.

Howard V. Finston, Professor of Organizational Behavior, School of Business & Administrative Sciences, University of New Mexico.

W.O. Fleckenstein, General Manager, Research and Development, Western Electric Company, Princeton, N.J.

William C. Flewellen, Jr., Dean of the College of Business Administration, University of Georgia, Athens.

E. Dana Gibson, Professor of Information Systems Management, San Diego State College.

Irving Gilman, President, Analytical Research Institute, Inc., Peekskill, N.Y.

Ross W. Hammond, Chief, Industrial Development Division, Georgia Institute of Technology, Atlanta.

James C. Hetrick, Senior Staff Consultant, Arthur D. Little, Inc., Cambridge, Mass.

Gale Edward Jensen, Professor and Program Director, Program on Community and Educational Reorganization for Economic Development, University of Michigan.

Mary Conway Kohler, Director, National Commission on Resources for Youth Inc., New York.

Edward F. Lannigan, Vice President-Industrial Relations., Reliance Electric Company, Cleveland, O.

Frank M. Leonard, Consultant, Technical Staff, Systems Science Corporation, Silver Spring, Md.

Richard S. Lewis, Managing Editor, Bulletin of the Atomic Scientists, Chicago.

J. Allan MacLean, President, Dodge Manufacturing Corporation, Division of Reliance Electric Company, Mishawaka, Ind.

J. Harry Mobley, Colonel, U.S. Army; Staff Assistant, Office of the Assistant Secretary of Defense for International Affairs, Washington

William G. Pollard, Executive Director, Oak Ridge Associated Universities.

Herbert W. Robinson, Vice President, Control Data Corporation, C-E-I-R, Bethesda, Md.

Emerson P. Schmidt, Economic Consultant, Oakton, Va.

Ben B. Seligman, Professor of Economics and Director, Labor Relations and Research Center, University of Massachusetts.

Vladimir Slamecka, Professor and Director, School of Information Science, Georgia Institute of Technology, Atlanta.

Donald T. Soule, Vice President and General Manager, Haughton Elevator Company, Division of Reliance Electric Company, Toledo, O.

William L. Swager, Associate Manager, Department of Economics, Columbus Laboratories, Battelle Memorial Institute, Columbus, O.

George Terborgh, Research Director, Machinery and Allied Products Institute, Washington.

Peter J. Tsivitse, Chief Engineer-Rotating Machinery, Research and Development, Reliance Electric Company, Cleveland, O.

Thomas L. Whisler, Professor of Industrial Relations, Graduate School of Business, University of Chicago.

James O. White, Director of Government Finance Relations, Lockheed Aircraft Corporation, Burbank, Calif.

Richard S. White, President, Automation Engineering Laboratory, Inc., Wilton, Conn.

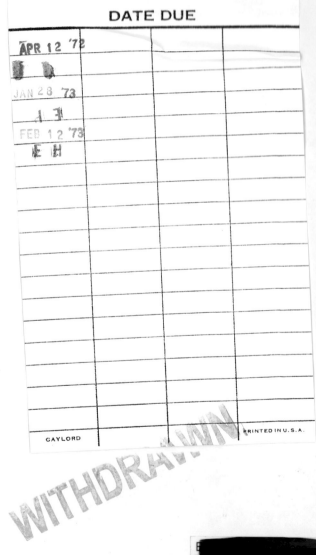